Landmark Countryside Collection

THE WINDMILLS OF THOMAS HENNELL

By Alan Stoyel

THE WINDMILLS OF
THOMAS HENNELL

By Alan Stoyel

====== Published by ======

Ashbourne Hall, Cokayne Ave
Ashbourne, Derbyshire DE6 1EJ England
Tel: (01335) 347349 Fax: (01335) 347303
e-mail: landmark@clara.net
web site: www.landmarkpublishing.co.uk

ISBN 13: 978 1 84306 224 0

ISBN: 1 84306 224 0

© Alan Stoyel

Front cover: Bembridge Mill, Isle of Wight
Back cover: Delce Mill, Rochester (Bottom). Moulin Deschodt, Wormhoudt, France (Top)

Page 3: Union Mill, Cranbrook, Kent. Pencil and watercolour, 548mm x 360mm

British Library Cataloguing in Publication Data: a catalogue record for this book is available from the British Library.

Print: Cromwell Press Ltd, Trowbridge.

Production: Michelle Hunt (Book & Cover Design);

Lindsey Porter (Scanning); Ian Howe (Editorial).

Contents

The name Thomas Hennell is familiar to a number of diverse people. His contribution to the art world is generally considered to be his greatest legacy, but this is spread widely. To some, it is his portrayal of rustic crafts and their associated artefacts in rural England that springs to mind. Others will think of his work as an official war artist. A further group will recall the variety of his writing. The books *Change in the Farm* and *The Countryman at Work* are memorable for text and illustration. He also wrote and published poetry, and, following a bout of mental illness, produced the autobiographical *The Witnesses*, a book of text, prose and illustrations.

The story of his life has been brought together in Michael MacLeod's definitive work *Thomas Hennell: Countryman, artist and writer*, to which all interested readers are directed. The acknowledgements in that book are testament to the breadth of Thomas Hennell's talents. His work then formed part of the collections of at least the following institutions: The Ashmolean Museum, The British Council, Canterbury Royal Museum, The Centre for European Agricultural Studies (Wye College), The Fine Art Society, The Government Art Collection, Glasgow Art Gallery, The Imperial War Museum, The Laing Art Gallery, Manchester City Art Gallery, The National Maritime Museum, The RAF Museum, The Russell-Cotes Museum and Art Gallery, The Tate Gallery and The Victoria and Albert Museum. The Museum of English Rural Life, at Reading, also has a significant number of his pictures.

The following is a brief summary of the major events in Thomas Hennell's remarkable life. Born on 16th April 1903 at Ridley in Kent, he was educated at Bradfield College in Berkshire and then studied drawing and painting at the Polytechnic School of Art in London. After a spell in London, he taught at Kingswood School, Bath from 1928 to 1932, and it was here he started to make drawings of country crafts and farm implements, which were later included in *Change in the Farm*, published in 1933. While at Bath his drawings were exhibited there and in Folkestone. It was in 1927 that Hennell contacted Rex Wailes, the acknowledged windmill expert. They became close friends.

Returning to London, he suffered a nervous breakdown, requiring a long stay in hospital, and it was not until 1935 that he returned to Ridley. He then recorded many of his experiences during his illness in *The Witnesses*, published in 1938. He also wrote poems, which were published in 1936.

In the period 1938–43 Thomas Hennell received various commissions for drawings and paintings, culminating in periods spent abroad as an official war artist. One was in Iceland in 1943 and another in 1944–5 when, attached to the Royal Navy, he made watercolours in northern France, Belgium and Holland. In 1945 he flew to India, this time attached to the Royal Air Force, to record aspects of the war in India and Burma. While there, he was captured by Indonesian terrorists in Java. He was last seen on 5th November 1945. At the age of 42, he disappeared without trace.

ACKNOWLEDGEMENTS

Rex Wailes, the celebrated expert on windmills, deserves special mention here. Without his influence many of these drawings and paintings would never have been produced. Particular thanks are due to Anthea de Barton-Watson, Rex Wailes's daughter. She is the owner of all the works of art included here, and has been kind enough to allow the use of them for this book. I am also pleased to express special gratitude to Martin Watts for much advice and help, Gareth Hughes for making available his unpublished research on windmills in north-west England, Vincent Pargeter for help on technical matters, and Luke Bonwick, Mildred Cookson, Roy Gregory, Simon Hudson, Kenneth Major and James Waterfield for their individual contributions. For information on the Irish subjects assistance has kindly been given by Fred Hamond, Stephanie Bourke and William Hogg. I should also like to thank Lindsey Porter for his help and encouragement. Finally, I am especially grateful to Critchell Britten for her helpful and constructive criticism, and her patience.

part from bringing to light a private collection of windmill drawings and paintings by an acknowledged artist, this book aims to provide as full an explanation as possible of the subjects. This requires an assessment of each picture, and, since many of these can only be described as technical drawings, they require technical explanations. The author has been involved with mills for over fifty years, knew Rex Wailes and his family, and was instrumental in rescuing some of the drawings in question. He therefore feels privileged in taking on this task. It must be stressed, however, that the explanatory captions are written, not by an art expert, but by someone with technical experience of, and a passion for, traditional mills.

These drawings capture the spirit and detail better than could have been achieved with a camera. Features have been emphasised or subdued where thought necessary, and sometimes a choice of viewpoint or perspective has been changed, each operation done with great effect. Very occasionally the proportions of an object have slipped, a perspective is strained, or something vital has not been completed. In one or two cases, where a detail has been missed or drawn in a puzzling way, the viewer has to question whether, for once, Hennell really understood the particular operation precisely – or perhaps he was not paying attention to the function of something that he considered ephemeral to the subject of the particular picture. Despite such very occasional shortcomings, these drawings and paintings form a unique record. Many of the windmills have disappeared long ago; some have been lost relatively recently. Every one will have changed, albeit subtly.

Many of these drawings were never intended to be seen in their present state – if at all. Despite their sketchy form they go beyond creating a straightforward record of the subject. Hennell's drawings seem to be an extension of the skills of the men who created the working parts of these windmills – that is why they work so well. His respect and appreciation of traditional rural craftsmanship has given us unforgettable drawings of agricultural wagons – some of which grace the pages of *Change in the Farm*. In his windmills there is the same ease of expression conveyed by the simplest lines. He has a razor-sharp eye for detail, but, apart from his earliest work, he never produces anything tight or fussy. There is that combination of freedom of line and accuracy of form, giving an incomparable feeling of the third dimension.

Almost the entire private collection of Hennell's windmill drawings feature in this portfolio. It is very subjective, as would be expected. For example, Norfolk, the county which comes to the minds of so many people as soon as the word "windmill" is mentioned, has only two of its mills featured here. However, the subjectivity is a bonus, as the artist has been able to bring in such a variety of different geographical areas. He thus shows a remarkably wide spectrum of the various types of windmill; exhibiting the local variations of their working parts. It was this traditional millwrighting that he found so fascinating.

Tide Mills in England and Wales (read at the Institution of Civil Engineers, 12th October 1938, and published subsequently by the Newcomen Society) was the first paper by Rex Wailes in which he used Thomas Hennell to illustrate the text, incorporating eleven of his drawings of specific features in tide mills.

The drawing in Fig. 62 has been published before in *Suffolk Windmills: Part I, Post Mills*, a paper by Rex Wailes, published by the Newcomen Society. Also included in this paper were nine other Hennell drawings from photographs taken by Rex Wailes. Since all these had only been reproduced in small format, it was thought worth including them in the present publication. In *Essex Windmills*, another paper by Rex Wailes, published by the Newcomen Society, two of Hennell's illustrations were used. One was a drawing inside Cutmaple Mill, Sible Hedingham. Since he produced two versions of this picture, the previously unpublished one has been used here. The location of the other drawing in that publication, of a detail at South Ockendon Mill, is presently unknown. *The Countryman at Work*, written and illustrated by Thomas Hennell, was published posthumously in 1947. It contained much of what he held dear, and included a chapter entitled "The Windmiller", with four drawings relating to Union Mill, Cranbrook. Three of these are included here.

It may not be generally known that *Windmills in England*, published in 1948, and *The English Windmill*, published in 1954, the best known of the various publications by Rex Wailes, were also originally intended to be illustrated by Thomas Hennell. The artist's untimely death came as a great shock. The earlier publication was eventually produced with most of the illustrations being photographs by Rex Wailes, but dedicated "to the memory of Thomas Hennell, R.W.S. with whom I had hoped to write this book". Too much was still required for the prospective second work to go ahead as planned. A fresh start on *The English Windmill* produced the fine drawings of Vincent Lines, a long-time friend of Hennell. Only two of Thomas Hennell's pictures were included, an impressive one of Argos Hill Mill, Sussex (Plate XVIII), and the line drawing of Eye Mill, Suffolk (Fig 14) which is included here as Fig 62.

These drawings and paintings were all given at various times to Rex Wailes, Enid, his wife, or Anthea, his daughter. The gifts were made either by the artist, Tom (as he was known to them, being not only Rex's close friend but also Anthea's godfather) or, later on, by Betty, his sister. Years after the death of Rex Wailes some of these works were found languishing in one of the numerous sheds in his garden, so their appearance here is given a special poignancy. Unfortunately many of the pictures were on paper of poor quality. Years of storage, sometimes in damp conditions, have left their mark. Some drawings were of a large format, too big for the particular receptacle holding them, so that they were folded. Many others have edges badly frayed and locally torn, some with holes where they have been fastened with drawing pins. The author was involved in salvaging the remaining part of the archive of the late Rex Wailes and safeguarding its future. Some of Thomas Hennell's pictures were recovered, taken home, and dried out carefully. There were other drawings, particularly some of interior features of tide mills, which were past redemption. Regrettably they could not be parted from their sodden surroundings.

The records comprising Rex Wailes's archive are now with the Science Museum, the National Monuments Record and the Mills Archive Trust. This particular collection of Thomas Hennell's drawings and paintings of windmills, however, belongs to the family; so it remains private property. It was thought that these pictures, and the historic information contained in them, were attractive enough and of sufficient importance to warrant publication.

This volume should fill a small gap in what is known about Thomas Hennell. It does not represent all the windmill pictures he produced, merely the relevant contents of a single collection. Here is a portfolio of his work, little of which has ever been seen before. Without doubt it constitutes a unique historic record of windmills. It is to be hoped that the text will help the appreciation and understanding of what he was conveying with such skill. Here is an opportunity to commemorate both the artist and his subjects.

Producing this book has been a challenge because of two contrasting types of reader. Hopefully the publication will appeal to some to whom Thomas Hennell, the artist, is much more important than the book's windmill content. Readers in this category may experience a steep learning curve! Detailed technical explanation is required because of the very technical nature of so many of the pictures. There are, however, readers for whom windmills are already an obsession. They may already know a great deal about the subjects illustrated. A further problem is that there is so much to see in the drawings that it is impossible to categorise them satisfactorily. The division into chapters is thus a compromise, although it is hoped that the technological elements are introduced in a logical sequence. However, at risk of duplication, technical features do require some explanation when they occur, irrespective of the chapter in which they appear. There is a glossary of windmill terms on pages 137–139.

Chapter 1
The Windmill In The Landscape

Windmills, as landscape features, are a natural magnet to many artists. They bring character to a view and, despite their industrial function, their traditional form is in sympathy with their rural surroundings. By their very nature they stand in exposed locations, and yet they have a look of solidity, an ageless quality that belies their vulnerability.

To obtain the most power from the wind the choice of location was critical. The more hilly the countryside, the more critical the location became. Trees, buildings, and even the ground, produce a drag on the air flow, and it became necessary to build taller structures in order to catch the wind where it was unimpeded. All this increased the vulnerability of the mills and their associated structures. The danger came not only from the wind, but also from lightning strikes. In addition, once a windmill had stopped work, and expensive maintenance was no longer being carried out,

it was in the most vulnerable position possible to be savaged by the elements.

Many mills have been destroyed by fire. The cause may have been lightning, mechanical friction, carelessness or arson. Whichever kind of windmill is involved, there is much dry wood, perhaps with some oil, grease or tallow to aid the conflagration. Ironically, with the taller stone or brick tower mills, the structure itself becomes a furnace chimney. Once any sort of windmill catches light the result is, almost invariably, total destruction.

We shall never know the total number of windmills that have ever graced the countryside; so many have come and gone without trace. Their decline is relentless, and the majority of those illustrated here have either disappeared or have been changed irrevocably (see postscript, page 137). It is a salutary lesson for us to respect the integrity of those windmills which survive.

Fig 1

Chillenden Mill, Kent

Pencil, 282mm x 383mm

Although a primitive type of windmill, this particular example is not as old as it looks. Despite its lack of height it is prominent in the landscape, due to the flatness of the arable land in which it stands. The whole body, or buck, turns to face the wind, the pivot being the vertical post, supported by its four inclined cross trees and horizontal quarter-bars. A post mill of this type, with an open trestle, as distinct from having a roundhouse as in Fig. 2, is an early form, and is now relatively rare. However, Chillenden Mill is an anachronism. It was the last post mill to have been built in Kent, replacing an earlier one in 1868.

Each sail is shuttered, with a prominent spring at the inner end, connected to the shutters. With a sudden gust of wind the shutters are forced open against the spring, taking the shock out of the system. These are known as spring sails, and were the invention of Andrew Meikle, a Scottish millwright, in 1772. The tension in the spring has to be set on each sail independently when the mill is at rest.

Soon after being restored by Kent County Council, the mill was blown over in a gale on the morning of 26th November 2003. Although it suffered appalling damage, it has been rebuilt, and given yet another lease of life. As the drawing is annotated "Chillenden (linseed)", it must be assumed that flax was being grown in the adjacent field, because this mill has always been for grinding corn.

Fig 2

Hartest Mill, Suffolk
Pencil and watercolour, 340mm x 244mm

This is a more typical post mill in more ways than one. It is derelict in this view – a fate which has overtaken nearly all the post mills in the country one by one. Because they are basically wooden structures in very exposed locations, they deteriorate rapidly. Another typical feature is the addition of the brick roundhouse. This gives protection to the vulnerable substructure and provides a very useful extra covered storage area. That there were two common sails (see Fig. 3) and two spring sails (see Fig. 1) is shown by constructional differences seen in the picture. The timber framework over the bottom of the steps would once have supported a fan for turning the mill automatically to face the wind.

Hartest Mill, between Sudbury and Bury St. Edmunds, was finally burnt to the ground in about 1958.

While the mill was being raised in height in 1810 an accident occurred and the mill collapsed. The two millwrights escaped, but an onlooker was severely injured!

11

Mount Ephraim Mill, Ash, near Sandwich, Kent

Pencil, 565mm x 455mm

Fig 3

A post mill, with roundhouse, this example is in workable condition. The sails, or sweeps as they are known in Kent, are complete, merely waiting for a fair wind and the cloth to be spread on them. Basic in form, these are known as common sails. At the back can be seen the tail-pole and wheel, for turning the mill to face the wind, and the lever on the pole, by which the mill steps would first be raised off the ground. The presence of this lever on a mill shows it was not turned by a fantail.

Mount Ephraim Mill ceased work about the beginning of the 1939–45 war and was blown down in about 1953. (For this mill see also Fig. 67.)

Fig 4

Thurston Mill, near Bury St Edmunds, Suffolk

Pencil and watercolour, 230mm x 305mm

Another post mill in workable condition, this one, erected here in 1750, displays a prominent fantail. This contrivance enabled the mill to be brought automatically to face the wind, and was set in motion in either direction, depending upon which way the wind started to shift. Fantails were frequently additions to existing mills, as in this case, as they saved much hard work, and removed some of the threat of wind damage. Thomas Hennell recorded: "bevel gears at each side of spindle of fan, working two wheels independently on gravel track." The top of one of the two tail-wheels is just visible in the picture. The sails are patent ones (see caption to Fig. 36), fitted with spring-loaded shutters which are self-regulating; an improvement on the spring sails seen in Fig. 1. The little porch roof is an attractive regional feature of these post mills.

The date of 1750 for Thurston Mill is reputed to have been when it was moved here from Pakenham. It had become derelict before the 1939–45 war and was demolished in about 1953. (For this mill see also Fig. 91.)

Fig 5

Wrawby Mill, near Brigg, North Lincolnshire

Pencil, 560mm x 381mm

Although similar to other post mills, this "Midland" type post mill does not rely wholly on the central massive post, but gains some support from wheels running on a track on top of the walls of the roundhouse. The roundhouse "roof" is, in this case, attached to the buck of the mill, and turns with it. Such mills were a feature of the Midlands but are now rare. The lever to lift the steps shows that this mill did not have a fantail. The drawing shows two common sails and two spring sails. The spring sails replaced common ones in 1917, having come second-hand from a mill near Grimsby.

Wrawby Mill was originally built in the late 18th century as an open trestle post mill and was converted to a "Midland" type post mill in the early 19th century. It worked by wind until 1940, but gradually deteriorated to the point of almost being demolished in 1961. It was saved at the last moment and brought back to life in 1965. The mill still works and is opened to visitors.

Wimbledon Common Mill, Greater London

Pencil and watercolour, 230mm x 292mm

Constructed like a conventional post mill, but with somewhat elevated substructure, the buck turned on a central post in the normal way. However, the drive from the sails ran down the centre of the bored-out post to the millstones and other machinery in the building on the ground below. A rare and complex structure, this hollow post mill was erected in 1817, but worked only until the 1860s.

In 1893, while under repair, the mill was found to be in a much worse condition than had been anticipated. The result was a virtual rebuild on the principle of a smock mill, with shorter sails, and most of the machinery was removed. It is now a milling museum.

Hennell wrote, probably in the 1920s: "It has not been in use for 50 or 60 years: the sweeps have been twice replaced: once just after the war, when two of them had blown off. They are about half as long as they should be, & I don't think they could possibly be used."

Fig 6

Fig 7

Tower Mills, Wick, Mid-Glamorgan, Wales

Ink, 334mm x 470mm

The tower mill was a later windmill development, in which only the cap turned to face the wind. This probably first appeared in Britain in the very late 13th century, at least a hundred years after the post mill had been introduced here. This drawing demonstrates the immense range of scale seen in tower windmills. The little, old one in the background would probably only have had a single pair of stones, and was dwarfed when the later, much more powerful mill was built, with two, perhaps even three, pairs of stones, probably in 1816. The remnants of a stage can be seen round the tower, which enabled the miller to carry out the necessary adjustments and controls from an elevated position when running the mill.

The tall mill had ceased work by 1890, and the cap and sails were blown off in a gale around 1894, the stage disappearing in a similar storm about nine years later. Since this was drawn it has been converted into a dwelling.

Fig 8

Mill near Dunmore, Co. Waterford, Ireland

Pencil, 230mm x 310mm

The solidly built but derelict shell of a tower mill is typical of this area. It was recorded by Thomas Hennell as being about 30 feet high, formerly with three floors, and walls 3 feet 6 inches thick. Despite its appearance, the mill was reputed to have worked until about 50 years before he drew it, and he talked to an old man of about 80 who had helped to operate it. The drawing is thought to be of Raheen Mill, about 7 miles north of Dunmore, overlooking Waterford harbour. Although it has lost its cap, the tower appears to have been to its full height in the drawing. The upper part of the tower of Raheen Mill has now been lost.

Rath Mill, Co. Wexford, Ireland

Pencil, 378mm x 558mm

Fig 9

Here is a small tower mill, still with a thatched cap in Rath townland, near Duncormick, between Wexford and Waterford. The marked batter of the walls makes a very strong structure, contrasting strongly with Watchfield Mill in Fig 10. Rath Mill was still at work when drawn, but driven by an engine, having had its sails removed. The mill had been re-floored, and probably largely re-equipped, when converted to engine power. Scales for weighing the products hang from a tripod outside. Of particular interest is the drying kiln to the right. The mill was marked on Taylor and Skinner's map of 1783, and both mill and kiln were specified in a survey of the 1840s, with the mill's height being given as only 22 feet 6 inches. Only the shell of this mill stands now, the external diameter of which, at ground level, is 32 feet, emphasising the extreme proportions of the structure. Unfortunately the kiln has now gone.

(For this mill see also Fig. 102.)

Fig 10

Watchfield Mill, Burnham Without, Somerset

Pencil, 354mm x 254mm

Here is another tower mill with a thatched cap, but showing a completely different local style. In this case the cap is extended at the rear to give protection to the mechanism for turning it to face the wind. The parallel-sided tower is in striking contrast to the preceding two Irish examples. Thomas Hennell noted on his drawing:
"… Thatched cap: wooden windshaft & brake-wheel. Stone bearing to windshaft. Double collar to stocks, similar to Kentish mills."

   Probably of late 18th century date, this mill had only a single pair of over-driven stones, but it lost all its working parts in the 1930s. The tower still stands, but its cap was replaced by a conical thatched roof in the 1970s.

Tacumshin Mill, Co. Wexford, Ireland

Pencil, 478mm x 400mm

Fig 11

This thatched tower mill, south-west of Rosslare, was still at work at the time of Hennell's visit. It shows very well the local style of sail construction, the bowsprit extension of the windshaft giving some extra support to the sails in the frequent westerly gales. A primitive mill, it has common sails, and was turned to wind by leverage on the long tail-pole from the rear of the cap.

Erected in 1846 by Nicholas Moran, Tacumshin contained two pairs of under-driven stones (see page 93) In use up to about 1908, it became derelict, but was restored to commercial use in about 1930, using parts from a windmill at Ballyfane. This new lease of life was short-lived, and it ceased work again about six years later, although a small amount of engine-powered provender milling continued to be carried out in an adjoining building. The mill was restored in 1952, and is now the only complete "original" windmill to remain in the Republic of Ireland. Privately owned, it is available for visits by the public, but it does not work.

"Tacumshane", as written on the drawing, is an alternative spelling of the name. Wexford used to be a county rich in windmills, due to the extent to which grain was grown, and the lack of available water power. (For this mill see also Figs. 50, 51 & 87.)

Fig 12

Ashton Mill, Chapel Allerton, Somerset

Pencil, 400mm x 317mm

A fairly primitive mill, built about 1760 on the site of a post mill. It is another tower in the Somerset tradition, with virtually no batter to the walls, and has required three iron strengthening-bands to prevent its collapse. In this case the turning to wind is achieved by pulling the endless chain hanging from the back of the cap. The mechanism above is so geared that the cap and sails can be turned in either direction with relative ease. The working parts were altered considerably in about 1900, using machinery from Moorlinch tower mill which had only recently been demolished. The alterations included replacing two of the common sails with spring sails and covering the cap with corrugated iron.

This mill ceased work in 1927, but it was restored in 1958 and is now opened to the public.
(For this mill see also Figs. 79, 80, 85 & 101.)

Fig 13

Bembridge Mill, Isle of Wight

Watercolour, 286mm x 395mm

An early 18th-century tower mill which has survived intact, showing the local style of cap – so different from some of the elegant examples in eastern England. There are four common sails, and the wheel at the back is to take the endless chain for turning the cap to wind.

The mill ceased work in 1913, having produced only animal feed since 1897. The derelict structure was painted by Hennell in September 1926, and it remained like this until 1957. Most of the wooden machinery survived, and is of considerable interest, although some parts have come from other local mills. Bembridge Mill is the only windmill remaining on the Isle of Wight.
It is now owned by The National Trust and is opened to visitors.

Sneath's Mill, Lutton Gowts, Lutton, Lincolnshire

Pencil and watercolour, 280mm x 385mm

Fig 14

Built in 1779, this tower mill is seen in its original condition, still with common sails, and a frame from the rear part of the cap, by which it could be turned to wind. This picture demonstrates the attempt that had been made to catch as much of the available wind as possible, and emphasises the starkness of the landscape. Advantage has been taken of a small mound which probably remained from an earlier post mill on the site. Unusually, this brick tower is octagonal.

The mill worked until the early 1930s, but was then abandoned. It still stands, although in poor condition, having lost its sails, but with most of its wooden machinery intact. It is now the oldest complete windmill in Lincolnshire.

Fig 15

Cemaes Mill, Llanbadrig, Anglesey

Pencil, 480mm x 316mm

This drawing, unusually, bears the author's name and the year, as if they had been painted on the beam supporting the shed roof. The mill is typical of Anglesey windmills, with its solid, battered tower, four common sails, and simple boat-shaped cap with a large external wheel with chain for winding. To prevent it swinging, the chain was attached to one of the pieces of timber seen projecting from the tower.

Cemaes Mill was built in 1828 and worked by wind until about 1930. Some grinding continued with the use of a diesel engine until 1946, but by then the sails had gone, and the mill was starting to deteriorate. In 1954 it was considered for restoration by Anglesey County Council, but, after a survey had been carried out, Cemaes was rejected in favour of Llynon Mill. Soon after this the machinery was sold for scrap and the floors eventually collapsed. Finally, in about 1983–5, the tower was subjected to a most unsympathetic domestic conversion.

Wellingore Mill, Lincolnshire

Pencil, 388mm x 280mm

Despite its uniform appearance, this tall tower mill was built in two phases. The brickwork up to the stage is much older than the 1854 date recorded on the upper part of the tower. There used to be four pairs of over-driven stones powered by six sails, although two of the sails had been removed by the time of this sketch. A mill could be worked with any number of sails, provided they were exactly in balance. A six-sailed mill could therefore keep going on any number between two and six, except five. When milling ceased in the late 1930s, only two sails were left in place.

By the end of the war the cap and machinery had been removed. For many years it stood as an empty tower, but, in the mid to late 1980s, the mill was converted to a dwelling.

Fig 17

Gedney Dyke Mill, Lincolnshire
Pencil, 380mm x 280mm

A very elegant South Lincolnshire tower mill, it was erected in 1836 and worked until 1942. The structure is a tall one and there were four pairs of over-driven stones. With such tall mills substantial adjacent or adjoining buildings could be added without interfering with the free flow of wind to the sails. This sketch shows it in working condition, with its full complement of six sails. The original graceful ogee cap, such a feature of the Lincolnshire mills, gave it a distinctive character.

Later, having lost its sails and its cap, the tower was re-capped to protect the interior, but this covering, too, was eventually blown off, to be replaced recently by a plastic cap. Despite the loss of cap and sails, the mill still remains largely complete.

Myer's Mill, Alford, Lincolnshire
Pencil, 280mm x 380mm

Fig 18

Here is an interesting view showing a fine complex of buildings associated with this six-sailed windmill. The mill was built in 1827 and, as can be surmised from the profile, its tower was raised in height, in 1889. In common with virtually all the larger mills, it had patent sails. These operated with spring-loaded shutters that were self-regulating (see caption to Fig. 36).

Myer's Mill was at work when this drawing was made, but it ceased trading in 1949. The machinery was removed in the 1950s and the tower was demolished in 1978.

Fig 19

Heckington Mill, Lincolnshire

Pencil, 560mm x 380mm

Although unfinished, this sketch gives an excellent impression of the scale and proportions of one of the larger Lincolnshire tower mills. It also shows the low outbuildings which often developed alongside the taller mills. This is the only eight-sailed windmill in England to have survived.

Heckington Mill was built in 1830 with five sails and three pairs of stones, but suffered from disastrous storm damage in 1890. The working parts of Tuxford's Mill, Boston, dating from 1813, were reassembled here in 1891. With four pairs of over-driven stones it worked commmercially until about the end of the 1939–45 war. Eventually, in 1953, Kesteven County Council purchased the mill and various repair programmes followed. It is now opened to the public.

Eye Mill, Cambridgeshire

Pencil and watercolour, 383mm x 283mm

This eight-floored tower mill had eight sails originally, as can be seen from the cast-iron cross on the front end of the windshaft. Latterly it functioned with only four patent sails until work ceased in the 1920s. It is reputed to have been raised in height in 1850. The tower was rendered and, unusually, the structure underneath was constructed of yellow brick. There was an iron stage to the third storey, and the mill contained four pairs of over-driven stones. Situated next to a modern mill, it was only grinding animal feed latterly.

The sails were removed in 1948, followed by the ogee cap in 1954, and now only the bottom three storeys of the tower remain. (For this mill see also Fig. 42.)

Sutton Mill, Norfolk

Pencil and watercolour, 290mm x 229mm

Fig 21

This impressive nine-storeyed, white-painted, brick tower mill, with its stage at the fifth floor, is shown in working condition. It is unusual in having a ten-bladed fan to turn the cap to wind. Constructed with four pairs of stones, the mill had a fifth pair for some time.

It was built by Englands of Ludham in 1862 to replace a former mill which had been destroyed by fire. Sutton Mill continued in use until 1940, when it was struck by lightning, not for the first time. After remaining derelict for many years, various repairs have been carried out from 1975 onwards. It is still complete, and is the tallest windmill still standing in Norfolk. Further repairs are needed urgently if deterioration of the structure is to be halted.

Fig 22

Scartho Mill, near Grimsby, Lincolnshire

Ink, 375mm x 278mm

A side-on view of the mill in working condition gives a good view of the ogee cap, five sails and fantail. The long lever projecting from the bottom of the cap is connected to a striking rod which passes through the centre of the iron windshaft, from end to end, and regulates the opening and closing of the shutters on the patent sails. The mill is at rest here, with shutters open. The lever is controlled by the striking chain which runs over a pulley above, drops to within reach of the ground, and runs back to the end of the lever. The two other chains or ropes dropping from the base of the cap probably connect with a safety catch on the brake for the mill. Both brake and shutters could therefore be controlled by the miller standing on the ground. A further point of interest is the external belt-wheel near the base of the tower. This could be used to take power out of the mill, to drive a saw-bench, for instance. The same wheel might have been connected to an engine putting power into the mill if there was insufficient wind.

This mill was built in 1869 by Saundersons of Louth, and Rex Wailes recorded that it was still at work in 1923, but that it was derelict 30 years later. It has long been demolished.

Fig 23

Tollerton Mill, North Yorkshire

Pencil and watercolour, 470mm x 630mm

A modest brick tower mill in working condition, it is significant in having roller reefing sails. Such sails are better seen, and described, at Preston's Mill, Seaton Ross, East Yorkshire (Fig. 43). The cap is turned to wind automatically by the fantail. The wheel and endless chain at the back of the fan stage is for controlling the roller reefing mechanism.

The date of construction is not known, but was probably around 1800. The mill went out of use in the 1930s and its machinery was removed in 1942. The derelict tower stood for a long time before being truncated and converted to a house.

Cap
Staining Mill-

Staining Mill, near Blackpool, Lancashire (Cap and sails)

Pencil, 560mm x 381mm

This beautiful drawing of the cap, and part of the sails, of the derelict tower mill, demonstrates another example of distinctive local style. The common sails are tapered, which is a feature of mills in north-west England. Beneath the straight-ridged cap are the short wooden boards of the petticoat which protects the curb upon which the cap turns. Locally visible through gaps in the boards, the curb is exposed to the elements. At the back of the stage is the large chain wheel for turning the mill to wind. This windmill, probably dating from the mid-18th century, was the last in Lancashire to operate with common sails and to be turned to wind in this way.

Staining Mill had fine wooden machinery, and only the iron windshaft survived a fire in 1981. A new cap was added the following year when the brick tower was converted to a dwelling. A kiln was part of the mill complex, but this, too, is now a house. (For this mill see also Fig. 98.)

Punnetts Town Sawmill, near Heathfield, East Sussex

Ink and watercolour, 288mm x 360mm

Fig 25

Particularly in the south-east of England smock mills became very popular. They were cheaper to build, and were less heavy on the foundations, than tower mills. Here is a smock mill typifying the traditions of Kent and East Sussex, particularly regarding the deep, rounded, boat-shaped cap – more like the upper part of the buck of a post mill. Unusually, this small mill drove sawmill equipment and was never used as a corn mill at this location, despite its traditional appearance.

Originally used for grinding corn, the mill had been moved to this site from Horam, about four miles away, in 1866. It worked until at least 1925, but after this the machinery was engine-driven, and the wind-powered part was dismantled in 1929. The mill was finally demolished in 1933.

Fig 26

Beacon Mill, Rottingdean, near Brighton, East Sussex

Watercolour, 378mm x 250mm

The majority of smock mills were constructed on an octagonal brick base, as shown in this picture, which was painted in August 1936. The building has been repaired a number of times, and has lost many of its working parts, including its fantail, but it is still a dramatic landscape feature. From the continual battering of the winds off the sea, this structure has adopted a permanent lean to the north-east.

The mill is a remarkable survival considering that its three pairs of under-driven stones ceased work in the 1880s and it only narrowly missed complete demolition in 1890. In 1802 the site gained some notoriety when workmen, digging foundations for the mill, discovered a skeleton, which mysteriously disappeared while they were having dinner! Beacon Mill still retains some items of machinery; only the lower part of the building is opened to visitors.

Fig 27

Delce Mill, Rochester, Kent

Pencil and watercolour, 482mm x 309mm

Thomas Hennell was clearly fascinated by this impressive and elegant smock mill, which contrasted so vividly with its surroundings. He painted a number of different views, three of which are illustrated here. In this one showing the rear of the cap, the striking lever and striking chain for the patent sails are visible, although, for some reason, the fan is not shown complete.

The picture is dated 2nd August 1927. He returned here in April 1932 and found the mill grinding by wind. In September 1937 it was still at work, and he commented that it was "rough grinding of several sorts, chaff-cutting; miller Glover". He added that "its sheds, among the slate-roofed slums & break-neck streets, are like old barges, or the Ark on Ararat". When he drew the mill again in September 1940 he recorded merely that it was "in good order".

Delce Mill, also known as Glover's Mill, was built in about 1853 by Henry Payne & Sons, who lived in a house alongside and, after the mill had been badly damaged by fire in 1872, they rebuilt it. It had only two pairs of stones, but did a good trade, with the assistance of a steam engine in an adjoining shed. (For this mill see also Figs. 28 & 29.)

Fig 28

Delce Mill, Rochester, Kent

Watercolour, 477mm x 309mm

The brick base of the mill had been extended upwards, so that the wooden structure was well above the level of adjacent buildings – as is clearly seen in this painting. In front of the windmill is the square brick chimney for the steam engine.

In 1897 a modern roller-mill of one sack per hour capacity was added by Henry Simon Ltd of Manchester, powered by the steam engine, but the windmill still remained in use until 1943. After it had become unsafe, the mill was demolished in 1955, although the brick base lasted until the early 1970s. The site is now built over. (For this mill see also Figs. 27 & 29.)

Base of mill, Delce Mill, Rochester, Kent

Pencil and watercolour, 321mm x 410mm

Fig 29

This shows the sprawl of buildings around the mill, and the necessity for the extended brick base. The shed which used to house the steam engine was the one adjacent to the mill on the far side. This engine was added as auxiliary power for the windmill, but later was used to drive the roller plant. The prominent square brick chimney stack can be seen in Fig. 28. (For this mill see also Figs. 27 & 28.)

Fig 30

Meopham Mill, Kent

Pencil, 475mm x 310mm

Here is another smock mill on an extended brick base, but it is unusual in having only six sides. The focal point of the community, and standing by the village green, Meopham Mill is reputed to date from 1801, but possibly was not erected until 1821. It was built with two pairs of under-driven stones, but another pair was added later. For many years the mill operated with only two of its four sails, and Thomas Hennell caught it in its last days of operation by wind, producing this dramatic sketch on 19th March 1927. Within a year the sole motive power had become an oil engine, later superseded by an electric motor.

Kent County Council acquired the mill in 1960. It was then extensively repaired and is now opened regularly.

Union Mill, Cranbrook, Kent

Ink, 440mm x 478mm

Fig 31

This drawing featured in *The Countryman at Work* and it demonstrates the impressive scale of the mill, seen overlooking the houses. Union Mill is the tallest smock mill in the country, the three-storeyed brick base taking the wooden smock well clear of the village rooftops. Built in 1814, it had three pairs of stones, and worked commercially until the 1950s. Some modernisation was carried out in 1840, including the addition of a fantail, and a steam engine was added in about 1863. Until it became the property of Kent County Council, Union Mill had been in the Russell family since 1832, and John Russell, the last owner, was an old friend of Rex Wailes. It is hardly surprising that there are six pictures here, in and around this mill. Thomas Hennell wrote to Rex Wailes in November 1941 and mentioned that he had done three drawings of the mill the previous week, at which time it was working, but not by wind.

(For this mill see also Frontispiece & Figs 32, 76, 97 & 116.)

Fig 32

Union Mill, Cranbrook, Kent

Pencil, 550mm x 361mm

The second picture is a similar view to the frontispiece, although it has the cap facing in a very different direction, showing details of its construction. The fantail, which was added in 1840, is clearly seen, but also visible is the chain-operated wheel below the far side, which was the original hand-operated method of turning the cap to wind. The other carries the chain to the striking mechanism for the patent sails. The striking chain has its weight hanging at the bottom, easily within reach of the miller when standing on the stage. (For an explanation of these features see the caption to Fig. 36.) Below the stage, on the hexagonal brick base, is the stone carrying the 1814 date. (For this mill see also Frontispiece & Figs. 31, 76, 97 & 116.)

Union Mill is still complete and opens to the public, but its superiority as a landscape feature has been seriously reduced by nearby misplaced and short-sighted modern development.

Moulin de Clairmarais, near St. Omer, Nord-Pas-de-Calais, France

Ink & watercolour, 230mm x 338mm

Fig 33

The tower mill appears to be complete, with a braced tail-pole for turning the local design of cap to face the wind. The picture is dated 1944 and is in a style which is typical for this period of Hennell's life, spent as a war artist. Presumably it was done in a snatched period of relaxation while on active service in northern France. Sketchy, but with characteristically bold lines, the watercolour is restricted to two shades of grey, just enough to contribute a third dimension to the drawing. He is not thinking about how the mill functioned, or of Rex Wailes and the forthcoming book. This picture is different from all the other pictures in the collection. Not only has this mill become part of the landscape, as distinct from being the subject of the picture, but the style has changed, and become much more impressionistic.

Chapter 2
Harnessing The Wind

The insatiable demand for more power brought the windmill into, and beyond, the so-called "industrial revolution". The search for ways to improve the efficiency of catching the free wind has produced many new ideas, but relatively few have reached fruition, and fewer still have lasted the course. To obtain power from the wind is only one consideration. To have the ability to control it is the real problem. The unpredictable and potentially devastating nature of this power source has also had a hand in defining the course of evolution of the windmill.

One major problem was to ensure the sails were always facing the wind. Not only was this the only means of obtaining significant power, but it presented the most streamlined elevation of the building to the weather. What is more, if the miller was caught unawares, and the wind blew strongly from the rear, the mill was at its most vulnerable to damage. Such a situation, known as being "tail-winded", has been the cause of irreparable structural and mechanical damage to a large number of windmills. The invention of the fantail in the 18th century, which automatically turned a post mill, or the cap of a tower or smock mill, to face the wind, was a tremendous boon. Fantails were added to the majority of windmills in this country, and must have saved a significant number of them from destruction, although the device was not foolproof.

The following drawings illustrate some of the ways in which problems associated with catching and controlling the wind were overcome by the millwrights. Tradition and common sense have dictated that windmills have various features in common, but, as is apparent here, no two windmills are the same. Both in major features and in details there is a variety reflecting local traditions and materials. It is these qualities which give each mill its unique character.

The sails, Russellstown, Co. Wexford, Ireland

Pencil, 224mm x 438mm

Fig 34

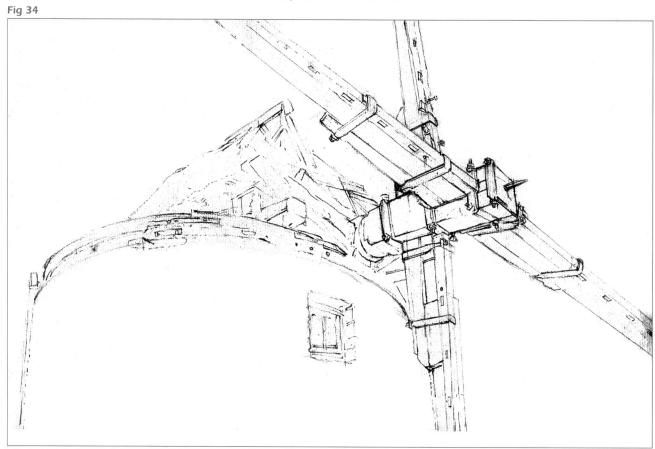

This is a wonderful drawing showing the traditional fixing of common sails to a wooden windshaft. The sails are mortised through the square end of the windshaft, forming a wooden poll end, with a series of grappling irons and clamps holding the whole arrangement tight. Visible in the whips of these sails are the mortises for the sail bars, the wooden cross-bars against which the sailcloth is laid. A wooden windshaft is now relatively rare, and a wooden poll end, as shown here, no longer exists on an English mill. The projecting spike on the end of the windshaft was probably to secure the bowsprit, as seen in Fig. 50. Around the top of the tower can be seen the wooden curb on which the cap turns. The curb in this case is a dead one, merely acting as a level, smooth surface upon which the cap frame slides. The thatched cap is clearly in poor condition already, and deterioration of wooden fabric exposed like this would have been rapid. (For this mill see also Fig. 72.)

Fig 35

Bekesbourne Mill, near Adisham, Kent

Pencil with watercolour, 330mm x 390mm

A relatively small, and very old, tarred Kent smock mill, standing in apparently working condition, alone in the landscape. The twist, or weather, on the shuttered, patent sails is clearly visible, a feature which gives them just a bit more thrust (for explanation of patent sails see page 46). The six-bladed fan at the back of the boat-shaped cap keeps the sails aligned directly into the wind. As soon as the wind changes its direction, even slightly, it immediately causes the fan to be set in motion. The shaft on which the fan is mounted is connected by gearing to turn the cap to face the wind again.

In 1922 the mill was tail-winded, and never worked again. It deteriorated rapidly until, in August 1933, it was completely destroyed as a result of a grass fire.

Cap and sails, Black Mill, Barham, Kent

Pencil, 380mm x 280mm

Fig 36

The cap of this fine smock mill shows features typical of Kent, including the arrangement of the fantail. The sails are "patent" ones, named from William Cubitt's patent of 1807. They are fitted with a series of pivoting shutters, the angle of which controls the resistance to the wind, and therefore the proportion of the wind's power that is utilised. The series of shutters are fitted to rods and levers connected to the front end of the striking rod, which projects from the front end of the windshaft (shown on the separate sketch to the right). This rod passes through the whole length of the bored-out windshaft and emerges at the rear, where there is the striking gear for controlling how much of the rod projects, and therefore the angle of the shutters. The striking gear is operated by the lever shown at the rear of the cap. When the striking lever is up the shutters are open; when down they are closed. On one side of the endless striking chain from this lever would be a hung a weight when at work. This weight would be proportional to the wind resistance needed to open the shutters. When not working, the weight would be hung on the other side of the chain, which would keep the shutters open. By this means the miller had remote control over the efficiency of the sails, as well as allowing them to give under excessive wind pressure. (For this mill see also Fig. 37.)

Fig 37

Base of mill, Black Mill, Barham, Kent

Pencil and watercolour, 292mm x 271mm

The second picture of this mill shows the miller carrying in a sack of grain on his back. The level of the taking-in door was designed for unloading wagons and was clearly no help in this case.

Although the mill would then still have been working regularly, it ceased about the time of the Second World War. It was later acquired by Kent County Council, and repair work was already in hand when the mill caught fire and was destroyed completely in March 1970. (For this mill see also Fig. 36.)

Fig 38

Cap, West Kingsdown Mill, Kent
Pencil, 255mm x 377mm

Despite the marked similarity between this cap and the one in Fig. 36, there are clear differences. The way in which the fantail is attached, for example, is a matter of individual millwrighting practice. That the fan has seven blades, instead of the six seen in the preceding example, is something of an eccentricity. Most unfortunately, this was changed to a more conventional eight-bladed design when some cosmetic repairs were carried out after its working life had ceased. A tarred smock mill with three pairs of over-driven stones, it was powered by two common sails and two patent ones. The striking chain and lever for the two patent sails can be seen protruding from the rear of the cap. The wheel just below the rear of the cap on the left-hand side is part of the fantail gear. This drawing was done in December 1929, during the very last working days of the mill using wind power. Subsequently an independent electric motor provided power for milling poultry feed. (For this mill see also Fig. 39.)

Fig 39

Lower part of mill, West Kingsdown Mill, Kent

Pencil, 385mm x 280mm

This is partly a working drawing with some dimensions written in. If not actually at work, the mill appears to have been in working condition, as suggested by the weights hanging on the striking chain where they can be reached easily from the wooden stage. The drawing is dated March 19th, and, although the year is not given, like the preceding one it was probably done about 1929.

The mill is of early 19th century date, having been moved from Farningham in 1880 at a cost of £800. Most of the machinery still remains in place and the mill is owned by Kent County Council. It is opened to the public. (For this mill see also Fig. 38.)

Upper part of mill, Stanton Smock Mill, Suffolk

Pencil, 480mm x 315mm

Fig 40

The cap of this smock mill is completely different in form and is a reflection of local tradition. The striking arrangement for the four patent sails is also different. The rack of the striking gear, which is engaged by the chainwheel pinion, is visible below the fan stage. The striking chain hangs down at the back. A further feature is the way in which the eight-bladed fantail is attached to the cap. A small section of the toothed rack on the curb, by which the turning was achieved, can just be seen below the front end of the fan stage. The iron windshaft was dated 1830, but had come second-hand from a mill in Norfolk.

Stanton smock mill was still at work in 1926, and was still in working condition when this was drawn. It had become derelict by the time Rex Wailes revisited it in 1939, and later in the same year it was demolished.

Fig 41

Frame for turning cap, West Wratting Mill, Cambridgeshire

Pencil, 455mm x 280mm

At the back of the "pepper-pot" cap is this massive frame for turning it to wind. This was done using the hand-operated windlass alongside the tail-wheel at the end of the tail-pole. This windlass wound in a rope, or chain, attached to one of the timber stumps seen projecting from the ground. Only two of the four common sails had been renewed as patent ones, which was not unusual. The controls for the striking gear for the patent sails can be seen behind the cap in this picture, but unfortunately these have been lost in subsequent repair works. Despite the fact that this is an octagonal smock mill, it is unusual in being on a circular brick base. The brake-wheel bears the date 1726, which is particularly early for a smock mill, and there are two pairs of under-driven stones.

The mill was worked by the Farrow family until 1924, latterly mainly for animal feed, but its condition then deteriorated. In 1957 it changed hands and it has been maintained in good condition ever since, preserved in a private garden. (For this mill see also Fig. 112.)

51

Fig 42

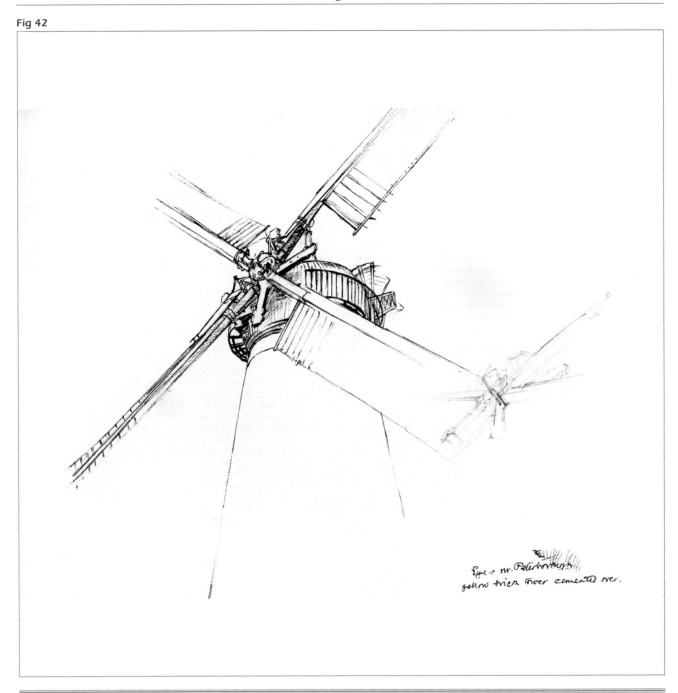

Sails and cross, Eye Mill,
near Peterborough, Cambridgeshire

Ink (with accompanying pencil sketch), 280mm x 378mm

The fixing of the four patent sails to an eight-armed cast-iron cross on the front of the windshaft is well seen in this excellent drawing. Originally an eight-sailer, Eye Mill worked for some years with six sails and, by the time of Hennell's visit, with only four. From the centre of the bored-out windshaft projects the end of the striking rod. The linkage from this can be seen, working through small levers and running down the whips, to operate the pivoting shutters.

Eye Mill was a tower mill of rendered yellow brick, said to have been raised in height in 1850. It worked until about 1925, but in 1948 the sails were removed, followed by the cap six years later. All that remain now are the bottom three storeys of the tower. (For this mill see also Fig. 20.)

Fig 43

Sails, cross and striking gear linkage, Preston's Mill, Seaton Ross, East Yorkshire

Ink with pencil, 458mm x 586mm

This drawing shows how the five sails of this tower mill were attached to the cast-iron cross, with quite a different linkage mechanism running to the sails. These were roller reefing sails, the eventual product of the patent of Captain Stephen Hooper in 1789. East Yorkshire was where this design became most popular, although no examples now survive in England. The longer levers in the linkage mechanism can be seen connected to a series of canvas-covered rollers which rolled and unrolled remotely. They were controlled by a similar rod to the one which operated the shutters of conventional patent sails, except that in this case the rod rotated. Both systems worked through the bored-out windshaft, but, unlike the patent sails, here there was no element of self-adjusting regulation of the sail's resistance to the wind.

The penultimate windmill to work in East Yorkshire, Preston's Mill was stripped of its working parts in 1951, very soon after it ceased grinding. The tower still stands. (For this mill see also Figs. 44, 45 & 99.)

Roller reefing sails and cross, Preston's Mill, Seaton Ross, East Yorkshire

Pencil, 333mm x 382mm

Fig 44

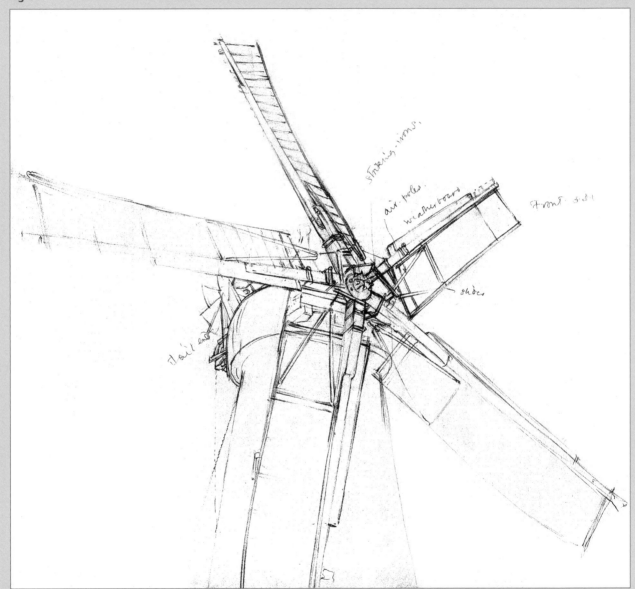

Here is another view picking out the relationship of roller reefing sails to the cast-iron cross, and the unique linkage mechanism in the gear connected to these canvas "roller blinds". Thomas Hennell has written one or two interesting remarks at the side of this sketch: "Canvas & band sails. Ship's canvas soaked in oil &c." and "The hindmost cross beam in the head is made of the upright of a post mill." (For this mill see also Figs. 43, 45 & 99.)

Fig 45

*Seaton Ross.
Yorks.*

Fantail and rear of cap, Preston's Mill, Seaton Ross, East Yorkshire

Ink, 380mm x 227mm

The rear of the ogee cap of this tower mill shows the fan and fan-stage and part of the associated gear. The horizontal shaft from the eight-bladed fan can be seen disappearing into the cap, enabling it to turn automatically to face the wind. The large wheel on the left, with the endless chain hanging from it, was for controlling the roller reefing mechanism via a rod through the bored-out windshaft. The other rope or chain, hanging down to the right, would have been for operating the brake.

Almost the last windmill to work in East Yorkshire, it is sad that Preston's Mill was gutted in 1951, very soon after it ceased grinding. The tower still stands, but now Ballycopeland tower mill, Co. Down, Northern Ireland has the only set of roller reefing sails known to have survived. (For Preston's mill see also Figs. 43 & 99.)

Fig 46

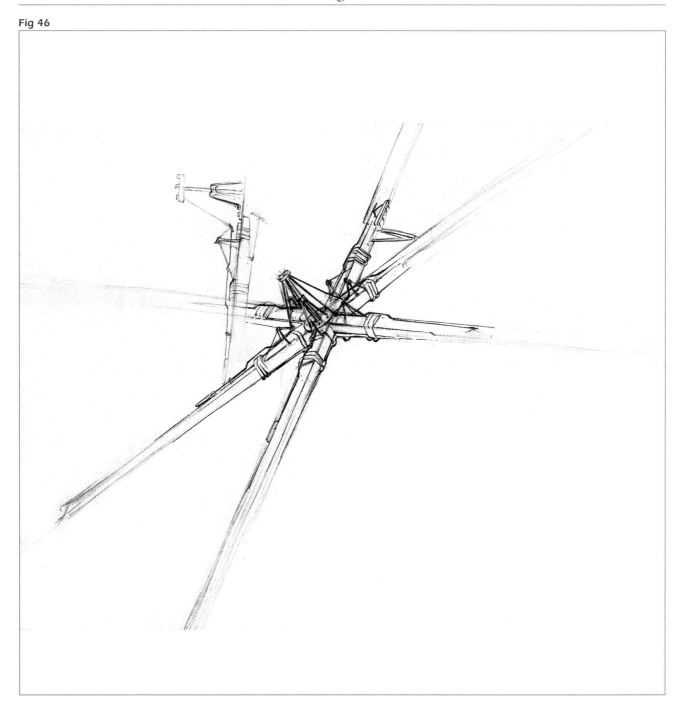

Striking linkage, Ingleborough Mill, West Walton, Norfolk

Pencil and ink, 280mm x 385mm

The linkage between the striking rod and the six patent sails is shown in detail in this confident drawing. The striking gear, at the tail end of the same windshaft, is shown in Fig. 47.

Ingleborough Mill was built with five sails in about 1824, but was changed to a six-sailer in the 1850s. It had four pairs of stones and probably ceased work in, or about, 1932, by which time it was running a half-sack Tattersall roller plant, with an engine supplying auxiliary power. The mill was dismantled in 1940, but the tower remains with modern machinery inside.

Striking gear, Ingleborough Mill, West Walton, Norfolk

Pencil, 280mm x 385mm

Fig 47

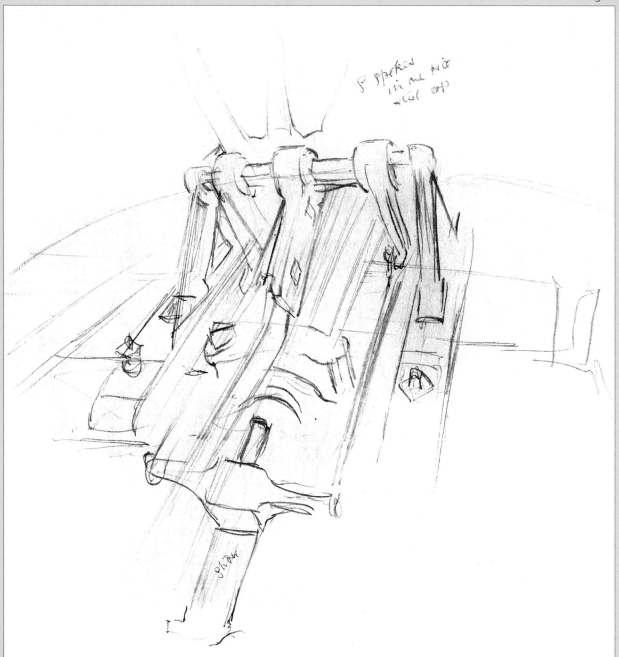

This rough sketch was drawn on the back of the previous drawing and shows the tail-end of the same windshaft. The tapering windshaft is in the upper part of the picture, with the striking rod emerging at the lower end and moving a sliding cross-head. This cross-head is linked by a pair of rods to cranks on a short cross-shaft near the top of the drawing. The striking lever, operated by the striking chain, causes a partial rotation of the cross-shaft, thus making the cross-head slide. This pushes the striking rod in or out of the windshaft, thus altering the linkage seen in the previous drawing.

Fig 48

Hayes Common Mill.

Striking linkage, Keston Mill, Kent
Ink, 362mm x 252mm

This drawing shows the striking gear connections in front of the patent sails of this post mill very clearly. By this ingenious mechanism a forward or backward movement of the striking rod is distributed down the whip of each sail to control the shutters. The couplings between the front of the striking rod and the triangles are sometimes known as the 'spider.' The shutters have been removed long ago. The sails here are not attached to the windshaft by an iron cross, but are held by timber clamps.

The mill stands on the edge of Hayes Common, thus justifying its annotation, although the structure is generally known as Keston Mill. It was built in 1716, making it the oldest mill still standing in Kent. It has two pairs of stones and is unusual for a post mill in this county to have had four patent sails. Working is believed to have ceased in 1878, so it is a remarkable survival, now standing in a private garden.

Fig 49

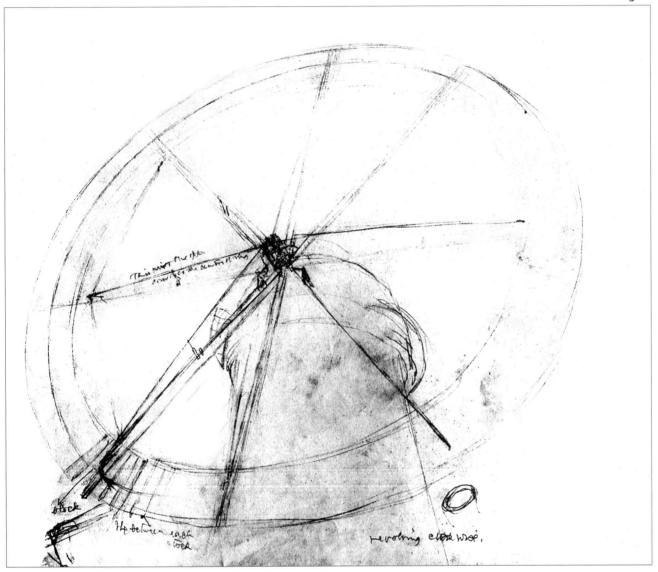

Annular sail, Haverhill Mill, Suffolk

Pencil, 277mm x 380mm

A rough sketch with notes of an annular sail, this example is one of only four known such installations at corn mills in this country. This sail was about fifty feet in diameter, supported by eight wooden stocks radiating from a cast-iron cross. Around the perimeter were 120 canvas-covered shutters, each 5 feet long. It was an original feature of the mill, which was erected about 1860. According to Hennell the annular sail was designed by the great-uncle of Miss Ruffle, the owner at the time of his visit. He noted that it was "revolving clockwise" and that there were "8 half stocks each one nearly filling socket of a grooved casting, plates on top fastened with 2 bolts, & pieces on the alternations for triangle from spider." (See Fig. 48.) He further wrote that the mill had "4 prs. stones driven from underneath."

This interesting mill worked until about 1933 and was demolished in 1942. (For this mill see also Figs. 59 & 60.)

The sails, Tacumshin Mill, Co. Wexford, Ireland

Pencil, 262mm x 382mm

Fig 50

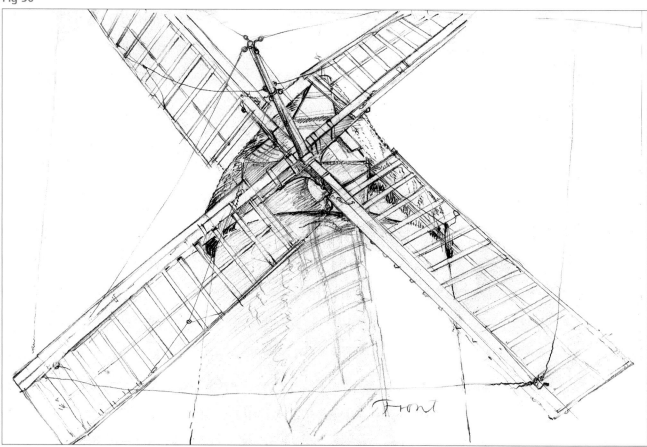

These two detailed drawings (Figs. 50 and 51) are early ones, probably dating from the 1920s. The front view shows the local style of construction of the common sails. The four sail whips are clamped to stocks which appear to be bolted to an iron cross, from which projects a bowsprit, a forward extension of the windshaft. Wires not only connect the ends of the sails to their neighbours, but also the sail-ends to the end of the bowsprit. Further wires link an intermediate position on the bowsprit to points on the trailing edge of each sail. All this is presumably to give extra support to the sails in a very exposed position. (For this mill see also Figs. 11. 51 & 87.)

Fig 51

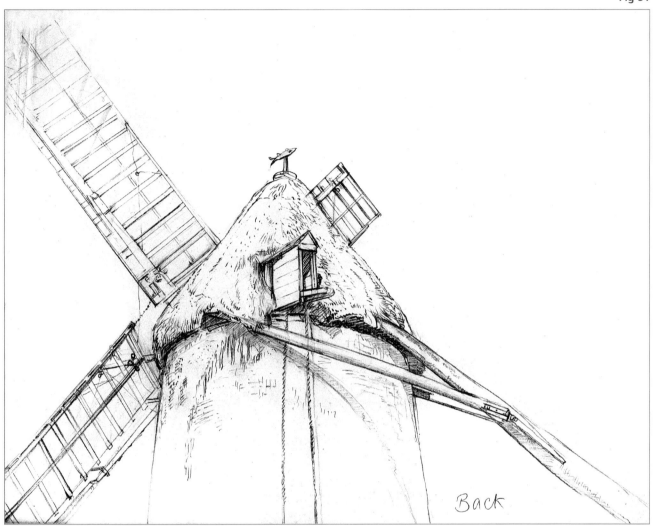

The cap from the rear, Tacumshin Mill, Co. Wexford, Ireland

Pencil, 300mm x 382mm

The back of the simple thatched cap contains a small dormer, from which hangs the rope for controlling the brake. From the rear of the cap extends a long, stoutly-braced tail-pole, through which the cap can be turned to face directly into the wind, lining up with the fish weathervane.

The mill was built in 1846 and remained in use until 1936. It was repaired in the 1950s and is opened to visitors. See page 20 for further information. (For this mill see also Figs. 11, 50 & 87.)

Fig 52

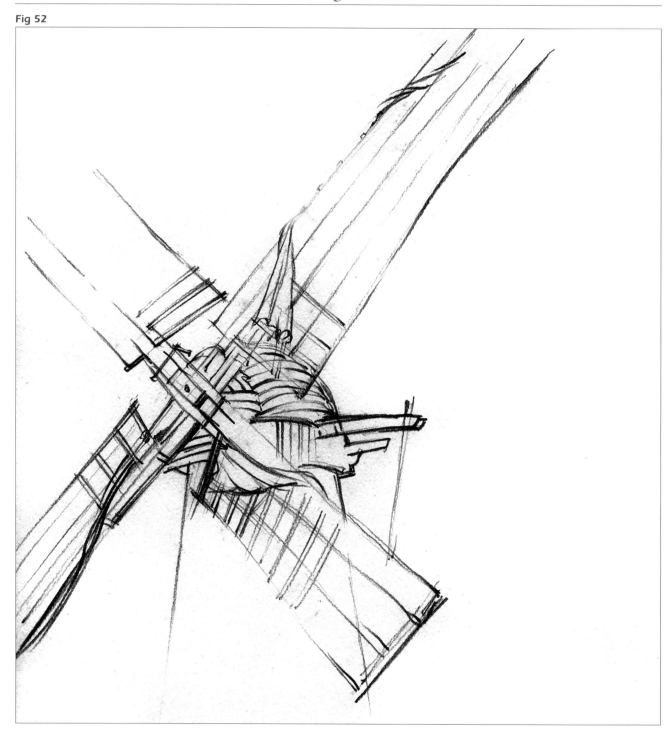

Fig. 52. Walberswick Drainage Mill, Suffolk

Pencil, 377mm x 254mm

This little drainage tower mill was still in workable condition when the sketch was done, showing each of the four common sails still carrying its furled cloth. At the rear can be seen part of the bracing attached to the tail-pole. A winch was fitted to the tail-pole for turning the cap to wind. The sails drove a scoop wheel, raising marsh water to a higher level, until 1940. Unusually, a pair of millstones had been installed at some time, too, to grind feed for the estate horses.

During the last war the mill was seriously damaged, having been used as a target for gunnery practice. Repairs were carried out in the 1950s, but in 1960 vandals started a fire which virtually gutted the building. This is the sad state in which it still remains.

Fig 53

Gearing of Tail. Willaston

Winding gear, Willaston Mill, Cheshire

Pencil, 560mm x 380mm

This explanatory sketch shows gearing for turning the cap to face the wind. It has been drawn from within the cap looking out towards the back. In the background is the wheel, over which passes an endless chain, for manual operation from below. As this wheel is rotated, it turns the small pinion meshing with the larger gear-wheel in the foreground. This larger wheel is on the same shaft as the second small pinion, glimpsed between the arms of the wheel, and this connects with the horizontal toothed rack attached to the curb on the tower. Kept well greased, this double step of gearing enables the heavy cap to be shifted with relative ease. Thomas Hennell recorded at some later, but unspecified, date that the mill had become derelict, the sails had been sawn off and the cap had gone, although most of the working parts were then still in place.

The five-storeyed brick tower mill with its four pairs of stones was built in 1801 to replace a nearby post mill. In about 1870 various outbuildings were added, including a steam mill with a sixty-foot chimney. The windmill was damaged by storms in 1911 and 1927, but continued to produce feedstuffs by engine power until the early 1930s. In the early 1950s it was gutted, and the outbuildings were demolished, followed by conversion to a house in 1958. It is ironic that Hennell chose the winding gear as his only subject, as it, together with the windshaft and cross, are the only working parts which have survived!

Striking gear, Brunswick Mill, Long Sutton, Lincolnshire

Pencil, 280mm x 382mm

Fig 54

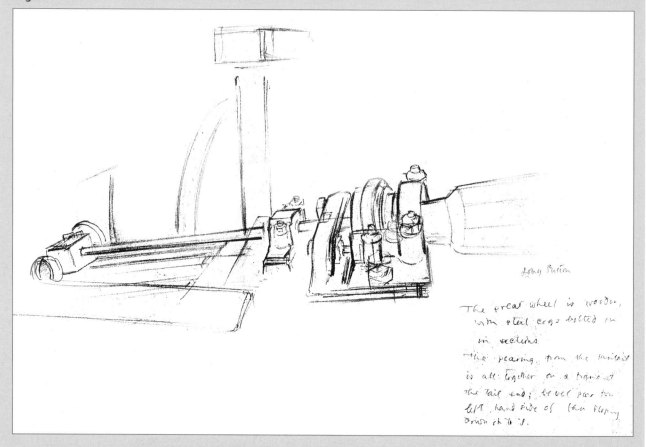

This view of the interior of the cap shows the striking rod behind the tail bearing of the wind-shaft, with a pair of wheels at the back. No mechanism is shown for controlling its forward and backward movement, however. The striking lever was almost certainly outside the cap, so would not show on the drawing. As the striking rod is fully back the connection between the back of the wheeled carriage and the striking lever may not have been visible, or Hennell may have chosen not to draw it for some reason.

Brunswick Mill was a tower mill of about five storeys, built in 1817 with four sails. It was later raised in height and changed to having six sails, working until the 1930s. Hennell noted that the spur-wheel was of wood with segmental iron teeth bolted on, and that "The gearing from the fantail is all together on a frame at the tail end; bevel gear from left hand side of fan sloping down onto it". Sadly the sails, windshaft and what remained of the cap were removed in 1973. The tower still stands, containing some of its machinery.

Fig 55

Striking gear, Willesborough Mill, Ashford, Kent

Pencil and ink, 280mm x 382mm

A rather similar striking gear can still be seen in this smock mill. In this case the rod merely slides back and forth, without the aid of rollers, controlled via the lever on the lay-shaft to the left.

Willesborough Mill was erected in 1869, by John Hill of Ashford, to replace an earlier smock mill. It has four pairs of over-driven stones, but it was found necessary to add an auxiliary steam engine within only three years. The mill worked by wind until 1938 and, after years of dereliction, was purchased by Ashford Borough Council in 1990. It has been restored to working condition and is now opened to the public. (For this mill see also Fig. 75.)

Fig 56

Outside and inside cap, Penny Hill Mill, Holbeach, Lincolnshire

Pencil, 562mm. x 380mm.

The fine ogee cap with its eight-bladed fan is well-shown in this composite drawing, and attention is drawn to a pulley at "A", from which hangs the rope for operating the brake. In the lower sketch, inside the cap, the same rope is marked running into the cap to the right. To set the mill going, the miller stands on the mill stage and pulls the brake rope, which rotates the wheel shown inside the cap. On the same little shaft is a windlass, on the far side of the wheel, and this winds up a chain attached to the rear end of the horizontal wooden brake lever. This lever is shown on the other side of the wind-shaft, and the fixed pin at the front end has been "dotted" in. Two steps of mechanical advantage have been obtained, from both the windlass and the lever, so that the weight of the brake system is taken up, and the brake, which runs around the rim of the brake-wheel, is released. It is a fail-safe system, so, if any of the linkages were to break, the weight and leverage of the brake lever would apply the brake automatically.

This was a six-sailed tower mill, built in 1826-7 with four sails driving three pairs of stones. In the late 19th century it was raised in height, and six sails were fitted with four pairs of stones. It worked until about 1940, was gutted by 1953, and now the empty tower is derelict. (For this mill see also Fig. 81)

Fig 57

Interior with striking gear, Westleton Post Mill, Suffolk

Ink (from a photograph by Rex Wailes), 270mm x 315mm

This is a view on the upper floor of the buck of a post mill, looking towards the rear, showing another variant of striking gear. By pulling down the rope to the far left, the long lever is raised, thus rotating the drum with the attached chains in a clockwise direction. These chains cause differential movement between the striking rod and the windshaft, thus controlling the shutters on the patent sails. The action of this drum is seen more clearly in Fig. 58. At the top of the drawing is the iron windshaft, in sections, bolted together.

Striking gear, Westleton Post Mill, Suffolk

Ink (from a photograph by Rex Wailes), 265mm x 210mm

Fig 58

The same drum and chains as in the previous drawing are seen from above, with the tail of the mill towards the top of the picture. In the foreground is the tail bearing of the windshaft, with the striking rod protruding from it. The drum is rotated in one direction by two of the chains, and pulled the reverse way by the other two, controlled by the long lever seen in Fig. 57. As the drum turns, it moves the striking rod relative to the windshaft, thus affecting the linkages to the shutters.

Westleton Post Mill was working when Rex Wailes visited it in 1926, but thirteen years later it was derelict, and was eventually demolished in 1963.

Fig 59

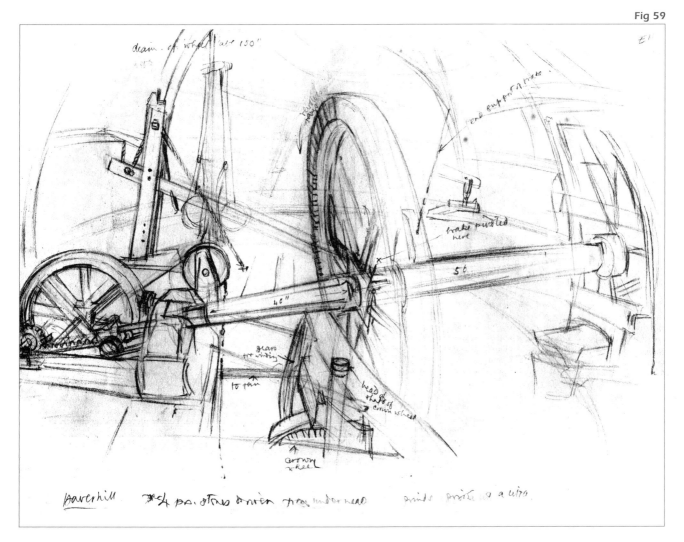

Interior of cap, Haverhill Mill, Suffolk

Pencil, 275mm. x 380mm.

Virtually all the working parts inside the cap are shown in this rough sketch. The complete length of the iron wind-shaft can be seen - from the central part of the annular sail, visible through the hatch to the right, to the striking gear to the left. In the centre is the brake-wheel, engaging the wallower below (labelled "crown wheel" in the drawing). Above and beyond the rear half of the windshaft is the brake lever, which is shown lifted by the rope - and therefore the brake is off. The 'ghost' of a pair of governors is drawn over the brake lever. Presumably they have been shown in this way because linkages were missing, and they were not part of any system then operating. The governors must once have controlled the opening of the shutters on the annular sail, but most likely had long been out of use. They had been replaced by the more conventional rack-and pinion striking gear shown in Fig. 60. (For details of the annular sail see page 59)

Instead of the fantail drive connecting with a rack on the curb at the rear of the cap in the conventional way, the drive was split into two by gears just above the wallower in this case. The drive was then applied, more evenly, on each side of the cap. Part of this system is indicated as another 'ghost' just above the wallower. (For Haverhill mill see also Figs. 49 & 60.)

Fig 60

The sails can be locked open or shut by taking the weights off the chain & pulling back the wheel; the block fits between A & B.

Striking gear, Haverhill Mill, Suffolk

Pencil, 280mm. x 380mm.

This is effectively an expanded view of the striking gear seen in Fig. 59. Here the striking chain passes over the small pulley and turns the double-flanged wheel, which causes the pinion to move the rack on the striking rod backwards or forwards. The shutters can be locked open, to be left securely inoperable, by pulling the rack as far back as possible and dropping the special wooden block, shown above, into the space between A and B (just to the right of the rack) on the drawing.

Haverhill Mill was the best-known of the four corn-grinding windmills in England to have had annular sails. Built about 1860, it had 4 pairs of under-driven stones and worked until about 1933. It was demolished in 1942. (For Haverhill mill see also Figs. 49 & 59.)

Fig 61

Winding gear, Weeton Mill, Lancashire

Pencil, 235mm x 368mm

A rough pencil sketch shows the winding gear to turn the cap into the wind, worked automatically by the fan outside. The view is from high up, inside the cap, looking downwards and sideways towards the right-hand side of the cap frame. In the bottom left-hand corner is the windshaft, with the brake-wheel at the left margin. Across the middle of the view is the heavy timber lever pivoting on the right of the picture, applying pressure on the brake that is clamped around the brake-wheel. The other timbers constitute the frame of the cap. Running down from the right is a shaft from the fan, with a pinion sandwiched between a pair of bevel gears on separate shafts running to opposite sides of the cap. The lay-shaft from one of these has a pinion (hidden beneath the cap frame timber) which engages the larger spur-wheel emerging behind the timber. This wheel is on another, shorter shaft with a pinion (in full view), and this turns against the fixed, circular, toothed rack (at the top of the drawing), thus turning the cap. Any movement from the pinion at the bottom of the fan shaft rotates both gears in opposite directions, imparting a unified direction of movement on opposite sides of the cap. This is a fascinating, but unusual, mechanism.

Weeton Mill was a four-storeyed brick tower mill dating from 1812, and it had an attractive inscribed stone to that effect on the east side of the tower. It worked until 1924, but was derelict thereafter. The whole structure was demolished as being unsafe in 1960.

Chapter 3
Inside A Post Mill

The venerable post mill is a massive covered machine, relying on stability. By its very nature there is a practical limit to both its size and power, and once it has gone out of use, its deterioration is usually rapid. Furthermore, its disappearance is usually total – at best only the roundhouse is likely to survive.

Inside, there is little spare room on either floor, and the upper one is a "health and safety" nightmare. The top of the buck gives enough clearance for the brake-wheel and, generally, for the sack-hoist driven off it. Initially post mills drove only a single pair of millstones, but gradually they were driving two, or even three, pairs, using different gearing configurations. As more ancillary machines came to be needed, a chronic lack of space was evident.

From the outset post mills were always vulnerable, particularly if not kept in good repair and turned regularly to wind. Once destroyed, a significant number would have been rebuilt on the same site as before, probably using the old foundations. With the demand for larger and more powerful structures many were replaced by tower & smock mills. Ongoing research and excavation is increasing gradually the number of post mills that are known to have existed in this country.

Fig 62

The substructure, Eye Mill, Suffolk

Pencil, 380mm x 480mm

A view in the upper storey of a two-storeyed roundhouse, this shows the substructure of an impressive post mill. The finely executed carving on the main post must have brought a wry smile to Rex Wailes's lips! The cross trees below and the quarter bars above can be seen clearly, as well as the construction of the roundhouse roof which protects the whole assembly.

This large post mill had three pairs of stones, two at the head and one at the tail. It worked until 1929, and was blown down in 1955.

Fig 63

Thornham Magna Mill, Suffolk

Ink (drawn from a photograph by Rex Wailes), 265mm x 235mm

This is looking forwards from the door in the lower floor of the buck of a very old post mill. The ancient post, upon which the buck turns, has been strengthened with numerous bands, and the buck itself is similarly braced. In the background are the two sets of governors associated with the two pairs of stones on the floor above (governors are discussed in Chapter 5). This mill worked until about 1940, became derelict, and was eventually burnt to the ground in an arson attack in 1959.

Fig 64

Six Mile Bottom Mill, Cambridgeshire

Pencil, 255mm x 380mm

The wooden windshaft has been replaced by a circular cast-iron one, as shown by the large, square, central aperture in the wooden brake-wheel. In this case there are two gears on the windshaft. The brake-wheel is referred to as the head-wheel, to distinguish it from the tail-wheel, which is out of sight to the left of the picture. Each wheel drives a single pair of millstones from above. This view is looking forwards towards the head-wheel, showing the bevelled stone nut on a short quant in the foreground which takes the drive to the front pair of stones. The top of the quant is resting in its bearing, or glut-box, but for some reason Hennell has not shown the mechanism which holds it in place. To the left are the horse and hopper feeding these stones, and above is the bell alarm, actuated by its striker fouling the head wheel (these features are dealt with in Chapter 5).

An inscribed "1766" on a quarter bar is a likely date of construction for this mill, although some parts could be earlier. The structure was moved here in about 1846 when the Cambridge to Newcastle railway was built. It ceased work in 1923 and was in a sorry state by the time that restoration eventually began in 1983. It remains complete.

Fig 65

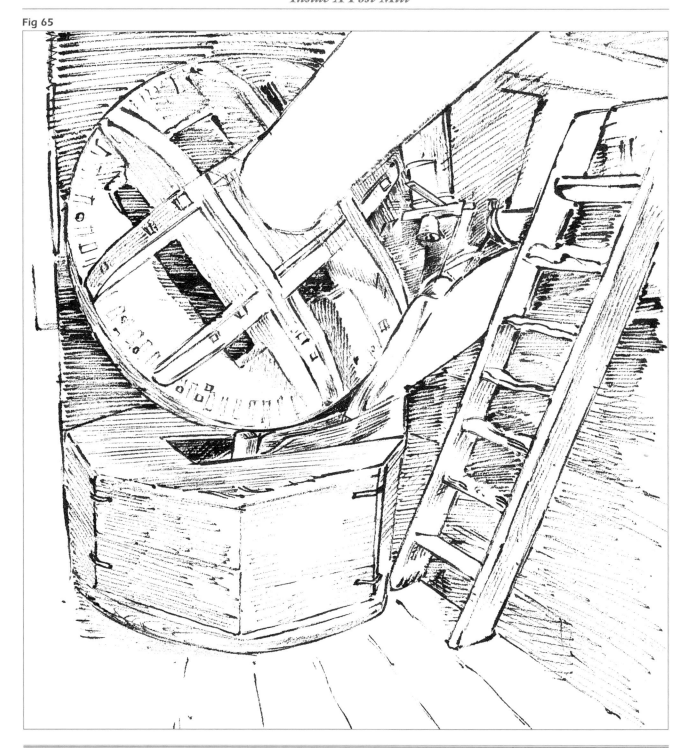

Tail-wheel and stones, Syleham Mill, Suffolk

Ink (drawn from a photograph by Rex Wailes), 270mm x 262mm

This view is on the stone floor, the upper floor in the buck, looking towards the back of the mill. It shows the wooden clasp-armed tail-wheel on the wooden windshaft. The head-wheel is on the same shaft, but behind the artist's viewpoint. Each wheel drives directly onto a stone nut above the millstones, although in this drawing it is hidden behind the tail-wheel. The tun here is octagonal, with two of the sides hinged for easy access. Lack of space has dictated a modification of the normal hopper and shoe arrangement to feed grain into the stones. The bell alarm is arranged with a stick which catches on the tail-wheel if the supply of corn runs out.

Syleham Mill was built in 1730 and was moved from Wingfield to its present site in about 1823. It worked by wind until 1954, and by engine for a further thirteen years, before becoming derelict.

The stone floor, Friston Mill, Suffolk

Ink (drawn from a photograph by Rex Wailes), 240mm x 280mm

A view looking forwards on the stone floor showing two pairs of stones driven from a central, short upright shaft. This is a post mill with an extra step of gearing. The brake-wheel engages the bevelled iron wallower at the top of the upright shaft, thus turning the larger spur-wheel beneath it – here shown with a protective guard around it. This drives the two small stone nuts on their short quants down to the stones. The bell alarm is arranged slightly differently, set in motion by a stick which drops, fouling the spur-wheel. A third pair of stones, behind the viewpoint, is driven from a tail-wheel. Friston Mill is built on a three-storeyed brick roundhouse and dates from 1812. It ceased work by wind in about 1959 and remains out of use, having come very close to demolition in both 1965 and 1970. (For this mill see also Fig. 107.)

The top of the mill, Mount Ephraim Mill, Ash, near Sandwich, Kent

Pencil, 414mm x 325mm

This may have been a preliminary sketch for a drawing. Various basic dimensions are given, although these were probably purely to calculate the height of the ridge – apparently established as measuring 33 feet 2½ inches. The view is looking forward in the top of the buck. In the ridge can be seen the sack-hoist and, beyond it, the brake-wheel, just fitting inside the curved boarding of the buck. The drawing conveys the rather claustrophobic atmosphere in which as much machinery as possible is packed into the small space available.

This and the following four drawings give an indication of the local variations which occur within a basic design; but not one of these five mills has survived. Mount Ephraim Mill ceased work about the beginning of the 1939–45 war and was blown down in about 1953. (For this mill see also Fig. 3.)

Fig 68

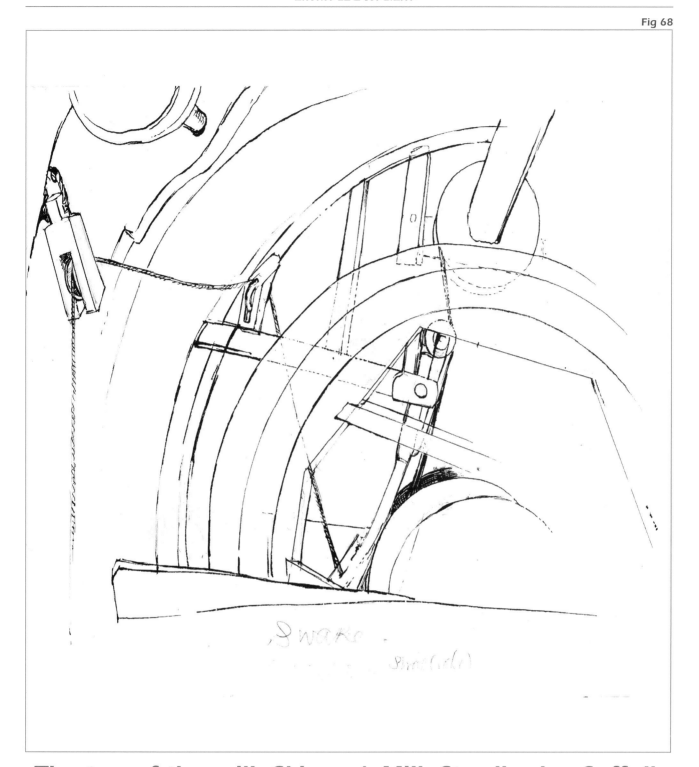

The top of the mill, Skinner's Mill, Stradbroke, Suffolk

Ink, 255mm x 380mm

Here is a sketch in the upper part of the buck, looking forwards towards the brake-wheel. To demonstrate the working of the sack-hoist, Hennell has, unusually, dotted in various hidden portions. At the top can be seen the hoist windlass, with a flanged belt pulley. This is set in motion by a jockey pulley, tightening the belt as soon as the control rope, seen on the left, is pulled. The power comes from the windshaft below, built up to form a flanged belt-wheel. Since this wheel is about twice the diameter of the one above, the hoist windlass will revolve at about twice the speed of the windshaft (sack-hoists are the subject of Chapter 6). The brake-wheel has been shown in outline only, but the ingenuity with which these working parts are fitted into the available space is evident.

This mill appears to have been in working condition when drawn, but it was demolished in 1942.

The top of the mill, Barley Green Mill, Stradbroke, Suffolk

Pencil, 255mm x 380mm

Fig 69

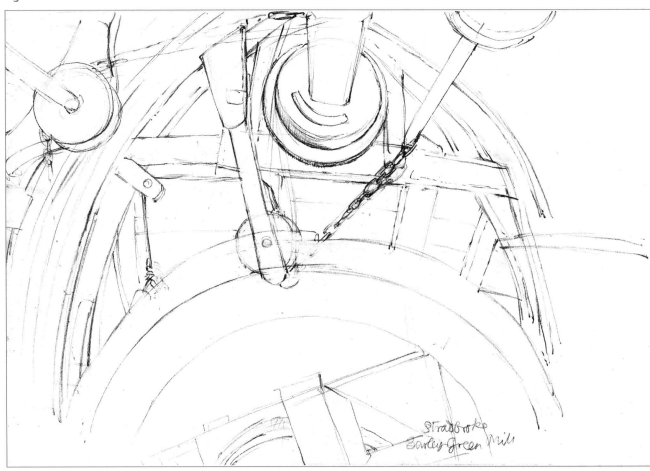

Another sketch from a similar position, showing the working of a sack-hoist, high in the buck of a post mill. This, too, is actuated by a jockey pulley tightening the belt. The hoisting chain runs from the windlass at the top, over a pulley at top-left, and down through the trap-doors below. The outline of the massive, wooden, clasp-armed brake-wheel is dominant in the lower half of the picture, and the attachment for the brake is visible above and to the left. This was a large post mill, rebuilt in 1777 with a two-storeyed roundhouse. There appears to have been more space in the ridge here than in the preceding examples.

As in Fig. 68, the mill appears to have been workable at the time of Thomas Hennell's visit, but it stopped in 1937, and was demolished in 1941. The fantail went to Drinkstone Mill, but all that remains on site now is the roundhouse, converted to a store.

Fig 70

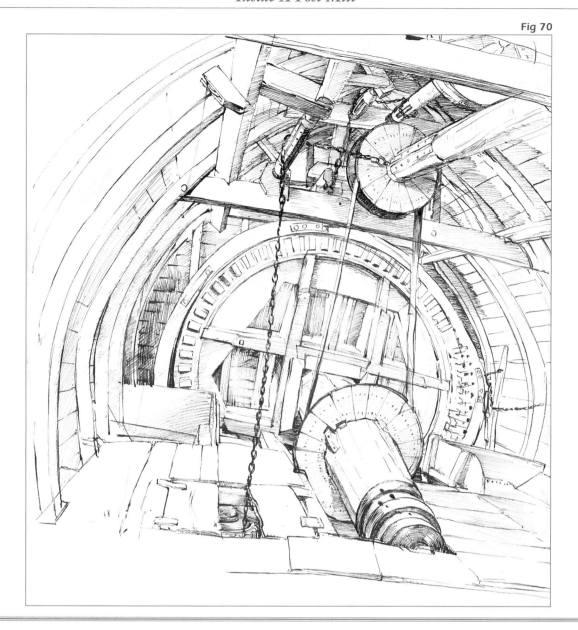

The top of the mill, Cutmaple Mill,
Sible Hedingham, Essex

Ink, 445mm x 415mm

This accomplished drawing, looking forwards in the top of the buck, demonstrates well the integration between the outer casing of a windmill and its working parts; the epitome of functional tradition. The wooden windshaft carries a fine clasp-armed brake-wheel, with the wooden brake clearly visible around it. The two raised wooden frames projecting above the floor, one on each side of the flanged wooden belt-wheel on the windshaft, are hoppers which feed corn to the two pairs of stones on the floor below. The sack-hoist is driven by a belt, with about a 2:1 ratio, and is set in motion by raising the beam on which the forward bearing rests, thus tightening the belt. The control cord to work the hoist passes round the wheel in the top right-hand corner, winding a chain onto a windlass, thus gaining mechanical advantage. This chain runs over a small straked roller and then drops to an attachment on the beam to be raised. The sack-hoist chain passes over another iron-straked roller before passing down through the sack-traps to the floor below. Visible through the gap between the sack-traps is the stone nut on a quant, driving the pair of stones on that side of the mill on the stone floor below (as seen in Fig. 66). The wooden windshaft here is shorter than usual.

Thought to have been built a little before 1775, this mill was moved about 50 yards to its later site. Also known as Metson's Mill, it ceased work in 1915, and was in an advanced state of dereliction when it was eventually demolished in 1956.

Fig 71

The top of the mill, Haughley Mill, Suffolk

Pencil, 320mm x 480mm

Another drawing looking forwards in the top of the buck shows the brake-wheel and other elements. The belt drive to the sack-hoist, again in the ridge, is taken from the windshaft ahead of the brake-wheel in this case. Also shown in the foreground is a wooden lay-shaft, driven by a wooden spur pinion off the brake-wheel. This powered ancillary machinery on the floor below by the belt-drive at bottom left. This mill retained its wooden windshaft latterly, but with the forward part replaced by iron, with an iron canister holding the sails. A modification to the wooden brake-wheel is clearly seen here. The original wheel had six wooden cants, each held by a radial compass-arm. This arrangement was later replaced by clasp-arms, but a mortise for the compass-arm is still clearly visible on the inner edge of each cant.

The mill was built in 1811 and appears to have still been in use when this drawing was made, but it was destroyed completely by arson in about 1940.

Chapter 4
Inside A Tower Mill And Smock Mill

The difference between a tower mill and a smock mill is purely that a tower mill is built of stone or brick, and a smock mill is its equivalent in wood. In both cases the basic structure is fixed, and it is only the cap which turns to face the wind. The tower mill first appeared at the end of the 13th century, but smock mills were introduced later, probably in the late 16th century, almost certainly from the Netherlands. Smock mills had real advantages, being cheaper to construct, of less weight on their foundations, and easier to move to another location. They occur principally in the south and east of England.

Internally the two types are basically similar, although regional styles prevailed in the choice of machinery and in other details. Both developed into tall structures, built to capture as much wind as possible, the larger smock mills generally being mounted on substantial brick bases in order to raise them to the required height. In some areas, however, the relatively primitive squat stone tower mills continued to serve the needs of their communities.

In primitive mills there is only a single pair of stones. These are positioned in the centre of the mill, in the uppermost storey, with a stone nut powered directly off the brake-wheel. In British mills, however, there is generally a second step of gearing, with the pairs of millstones arranged around a central upright shaft. This upright shaft is driven by the wallower off the brake-wheel, at its upper end, with a large spur-wheel further down. It is with small pinions, or stone nuts, engaged by the spur-wheel, that the millstones are driven – over-driven if from above, or under-driven if from below.

Internal view, Russellstown Mill, Co. Wicklow, Ireland

Pencil, 760mm x 557mm

Fig 72

This wonderful wide-angled drawing illustrates beautifully how all the wooden working parts of an old tower windmill fit together. It shows the clasp-armed brake-wheel at the top, viewed from the front, engaging the wooden wallower on the upright shaft. Below it is the clasp-armed spur-wheel, driving a stone nut on each side, connected to the two pairs of under-driven stones. The two stone-spindles are supported by wooden bridge trees which are fixed, and the tentering appears to have been done using the "T" shaped iron screw-fitting beneath the footstep bearing of each bridge tree. On top of the tower is a wooden dead curb, upon which the cap frame would be turned to face the wind, relying on well-greased blocks to reduce the friction as much as possible.

The stone furniture and any ancillary machines have been stripped out. The floors, and the stairs, have gone, leaving all the working parts exposed. This has created a unique opportunity – which was clearly an inspiration to Hennell. A mill in such a state would not have lasted for long as the thatched cap was already in a parlous condition. Close to eighty years later, nothing more than the gutted shell of a tower could be expected on site now. (For this mill see also Fig. 34.)

Fig 73

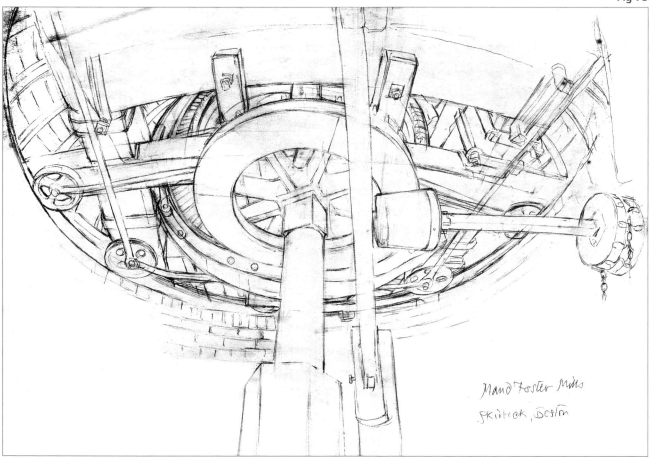

Maud Foster Mills
Skirbeck, Boston

Looking up into cap, Maud Foster Mill, Boston, Lincolnshire

Pencil, 380mm x 562mm

Here is a view from inside the top of the tower, looking up into the lower part of the cap. The curb is a dead one, and the series of wheels around the inside face of the tower keep the cap central as it turns. In the background, within the cap, is the elm brake-wheel with iron teeth, framed by the wooden brake. In the foreground is the iron wallower, engaged by the brake-wheel, at the top of the iron upright shaft which runs down the centre of the mill. The underside of the wallower is packed out with wood to form a friction surface, against which the roller is brought into contact, thus setting in motion the sack-hoist chain seen on the right-hand side. This chain differs from the other sack chains illustrated, in that it is an endless one with a series of short chain ends attached to it at regular intervals. It does not need to be wound up by a windlass and then let down each time. It is therefore much faster to operate – an important factor in such a tall and busy mill.

This is an exceptionally fine tower mill, still at work commercially, and opened to the public. Its scale and sophistication are in huge contrast with the tower mill seen in Fig. 72. Maud Foster Mill was built by the Hull millwrights, Norman and Smithson, in 1819 and has five sails driving three pairs of stones.

Looking down from the cap, Miles's Mill, Boughton under Blean, Kent

Ink and pencil, 390mm x 500mm

Fig 74

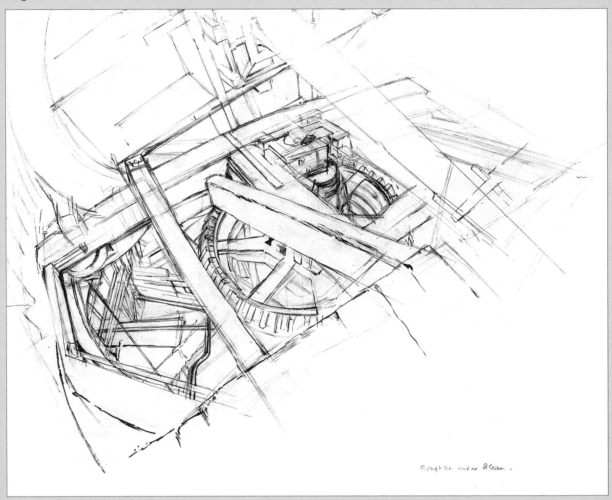

Boughton under Blean.

This unfinished drawing shows similar details to the previous one, although this time the view is looking down from the cap, and it is on a smock mill. At the top of the drawing and to the right are the wooden clasp-armed brake-wheel and the iron windshaft. Below the cap frame is the cast-iron wallower on the wooden upright shaft. To the left of the cap frame can be seen one of the truck wheels which run against a rail along the inside face of the top of the wooden tower, centring the turning cap.

The sketch is merely labelled "Boughton under Blean", and it is presumed to be of Miles's Mill. This was an old, and very broad, smock mill, the sails and fan of which were removed in 1929. The mill suffered later from bomb damage, and was demolished in 1942.

Fig 75

Upright shaft and wallower, Willesborough Mill, Ashford, Kent

Ink and pencil, 314mm x 480mm

Part of the brake-wheel is visible at the top of the picture, above the wallower and iron upright shaft. The wallower has a wooden friction ring on the under-side, just as in Maud Foster Mill (Fig. 73). To the left of it is the windlass of the sack-hoist, with the hoisting chain in the background. In the foreground, to the left, can be seen a long wooden lever, sloping down to the left. This can be raised by the rope at the left-hand end, which brings the friction drive into contact for hoisting sacks of grain.

Willesborough Mill is a smock mill on a brick base, just outside Ashford. It was erected in 1869 and worked until 1938. The mill has been restored by Ashford Borough Council and is now opened to the public. (For this mill see also Fig. 55.)

Fig 76

Brake-wheel, wallower and sack-hoist, Union Mill, Cranbrook, Kent

Ink, 410mm x 630mm

This is a fine view at the top of the largest smock mill in the country, and it gives a very good impression of the way the working parts integrate with the wooden tower and cap. In the centre, of both picture and mill, is the upright shaft and wallower, both of iron. Driving the wallower, to the right, is the brake-wheel, of iron with wooden cogs. The weight of the brake-wheel, together with the windshaft and sails, is carried by the cap – the lower part of which forms the top of this picture. Two of the truck wheels, and the circular track against which they turn, can be seen to the left. They ensure a perfect mesh of the brake-wheel cogs against the teeth of the wallower, no matter which way the cap is facing. Here is another example in which wooden blocks are fixed to the underside of the wallower to form a friction surface for operating the sack-hoist. The hoisting windlass and chain to the left are set in motion by the raising of the right-hand end of the windlass shaft so that the two friction surfaces are brought together. This is achieved by a simple rope and pulley system which lifts the far end of the bearing-support lever immediately to the right of the friction pulley.

Built in 1814, Union Mill had three pairs of stones, and worked commercially until the 1950s. Some modernisation was carried out in 1840, including the addition of a fantail. The mill is now owned by Kent County Council and is opened to visitors. (For this mill see also Frontispiece and Figs. 31, 32, 97 & 116.)

Cap-centring frame and wallower, Treales Mill, Lancashire

Pencil, 380mm x 560mm

Fig 77

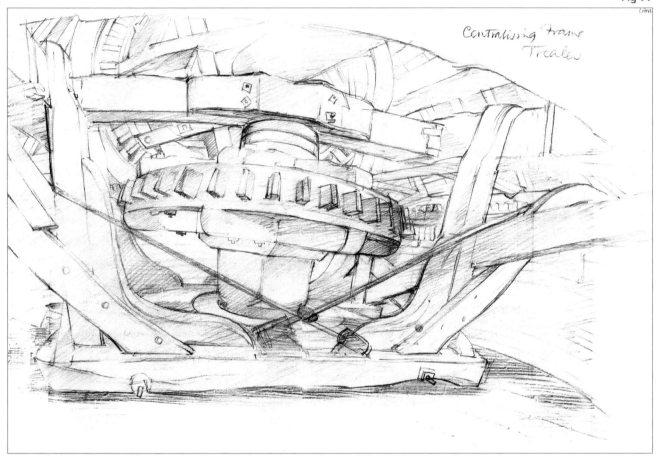

In the Fylde area of Lancashire, the Wirral of Cheshire, and in Anglesey, the cap was generally kept central by means of a wooden frame suspended below the cap frame inside the tower. This brilliant drawing is of one of these cap-centring frames, with the wooden wallower at the centre of the frame. The rack of the curb on the top of the tower is visible, more or less in the same plane as the wallower. This rack is to enable the cap to be turned into the wind. At the top of the picture is the windshaft and clasp-armed wooden brake-wheel.

In 1938, after the mill had become derelict, the cap was blown off with explosives. A conical roof was then fitted, but the mill was completely gutted twelve years later. (For Treales mill see also Figs. 78 & 93.)

Spur-wheel and quants, Treales Mill, Lancashire

Pencil, 340mm x 380mm

Fig 78

This is a detail of part of the gear further down in the same, over-driven mill. In the foreground is the quant, taking the drive down from stone nut to stones. It is out of gear in this case, with the stone nut disengaged from the spur-wheel. This stone nut is a lantern pinion, with wooden staves separating a pair of wooden discs. In the background is another quant, which carries a cast-iron mortise stone nut. The iron nut might have been a re-placement, or the lantern pinion could have come from somewhere else. It is not clear from this illustration how the drive is conveyed to the mortise spur pinion on the iron lay-shaft in the foreground.

Despite a date-stone of 1721, this three-storeyed, whitewashed, brick tower mill was typical of the regional style of the late 18th century. Treales Mill had five pairs of stones and worked until 1922. It was completely gutted in the 1950s, and was converted to a dwelling in 1960. As with the other mills in this area, it used to have a kiln. (For this mill see also Figs. 77 & 93.)

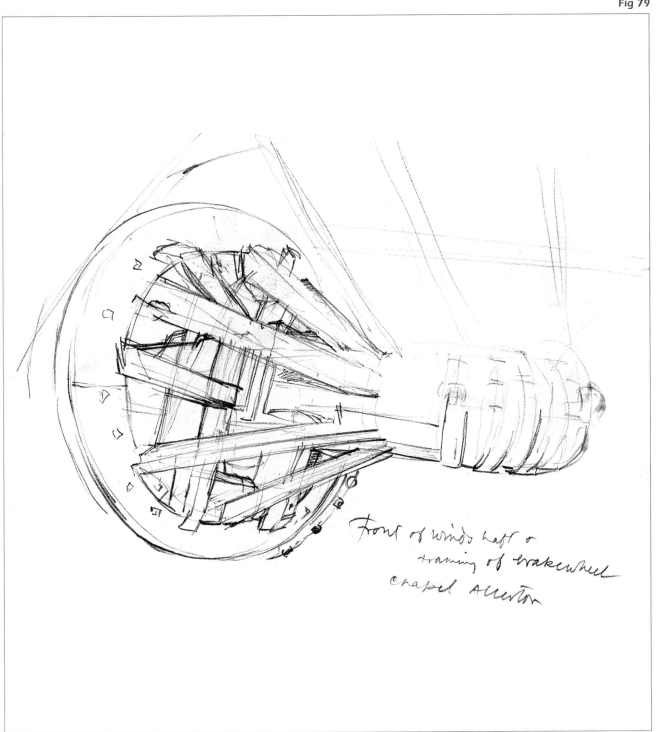

Front of winds haft & framing of brakewheel chapel Allerton

Brake-wheel and windshaft, Ashton Mill, Chapel Allerton, Somerset

Pencil, 254mm x 355mm

A sketch inside the cap of a primitive Somerset tower mill shows the front part of the wooden windshaft and the old wooden, clasp-armed brake-wheel with its braced frame. In time, some large wooden gear-wheels have a tendency to warp, preventing the mesh with the driven pinion being uniform, and requiring heavy bracing to force them back into shape, as here. The old wooden windshaft, too, is strongly banded. This was done to take an iron insert carrying a poll end for attachment of the sails; a modification probably carried out in about 1900. (For Ashton mill see also Figs. 12, 80, 85 & 101.)

Wallower and upright shaft, Ashton Mill, Chapel Allerton, Somerset

Pencil, 254mm x 355mm

Fig 80

This sketch roughly fits below the one shown in Fig. 79, the bevelled iron wallower on the wooden upright shaft being driven by the wooden brake-wheel. Immediately below this iron wallower is an earlier generation of wallower – a very old wooden one with its cogs sawn off flush. Most of the working parts were brought from Moorlinch Mill and installed here in about 1900. Before this Ashton Mill was very primitive, with a single pair of stones driven direct off the brake-wheel. After the remodelling there was still only one pair of stones, but now these were under-driven, one floor lower in the tower. The rebuild provided two steps of gearing instead of one, so the stones could work at a much higher speed than before. (For this mill see also Figs. 12, 79, 85 & 101.)

This mill was built about 1760 and finished work in 1927. Restored in 1958, it is now opened to the public.

Fig 81

Upright shaft and wallower, Penny Hill Mill, Holbeach, Lincolnshire

Pencil, 380mm x 560mm

Although similar to the last view, this fine drawing shows the elements in context, and in a larger mill. At the top of the picture is the wooden cap frame, resting on the curb at the top of the brick tower. In the centre is the wallower, almost at the top of the wooden upright shaft, driven by the brake-wheel in the background. The sack windlass and chain are to the right-hand side. In the background, on the right, is a smaller chain which controls the operation of the sack-hoist. When that chain is pulled it raises the bearing of the friction-pulley on the end of the windlass through a double-lever action, bringing the two friction surfaces together, thus setting the hoist in motion.

Penny Hill Mill is a brick tower mill, built in 1826–7 with four sails and three pairs of stones, replacing a smock mill. It was raised in height and altered to take six sails, and an extra pair of stones, late in the century. It worked until about the beginning of the last war, and was later gutted completely. The empty tower still remains. (For this mill see also Fig. 56.)

Fig 82

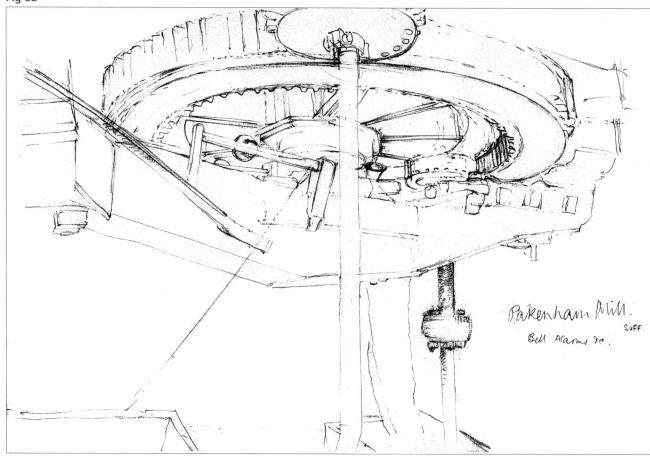

Spur-wheel, Pakenham Mill, Suffolk

Pencil, 255mm x 380mm

At Pakenham Mill this fine spur-wheel is at the bottom of the upright shaft, just above the millstones. It has a wooden rim and iron arms, and is unusual in being dished, with the rim and arms at different levels. This drove two stone nuts on quants down to the stones in the usual way. On the inside of the wooden rim of the wheel, however, is an iron toothed ring which drove an extra quant to another pair of stones. The runner of this extra pair was therefore rotating in the opposite direction to the two other pairs! Two different bell alarms are also shown, mounted beneath the spur-wheel.

Pakenham Mill is a five-storeyed brick tower mill, built in 1830. It continued working commercially into the 1970s, was restored to working condition in 1999–2000, and is now opened to the public.

Chapter 5
Millstones And Their Control

Millstones work in pairs: the bedstone stationary, and the runner stone rotating above it at a speed of perhaps two revolutions per second. The grain is fed into the central hole, or eye, of the runner, and is then ground by the differential movement between the dressed faces of the stones. The product, the meal, comes out around the edge of the stones and falls down a spout to a sack or other container on the floor below. A windmill in this country might contain between one and five pairs of stones.

The stones can be of various types, but the commonest are Peaks and French burrs. The Peaks were quarried in the Peak District of Derbyshire and Yorkshire and are for general purpose milling. The best stones for flour production are the French burrs, made up in this country from numerous cut blocks of chert, a flint-like stone, from quarries in France, the assembly then tightly constrained with iron bands.

When at work, each pair of stones is surrounded by a wooden casing, the tun, upon which stands a rectangular frame, the horse, supporting a wooden hopper containing the grain. This grain is fed into the central hole, or eye, of the runner stone by a wooden "shoe", which is shaken automatically in sympathy with the speed of the stone's rotation, thus controlling the feed. Most windmills had bell alarms, to warn the miller that the supply of grain to a pair of stones was coming to an end. This was of vital importance as the dressed faces of the stones were then in danger of touching, giving off sparks and starting a fire. Various bell alarm systems will be noted in these drawings.

Fig 83

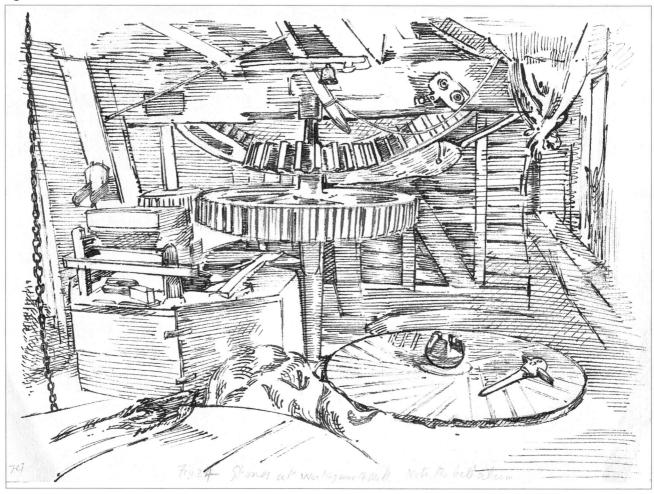

Stones, New Mill, Worlingworth, Suffolk

Ink, 190mm x 275mm

This view is looking forwards in the buck of a post mill in which there are two pairs of over-driven stones in the breast. The left-hand stones are set to work, with complete stone furniture. To the right, the runner stone has been removed and the furrowed face of the bedstone is exposed for dressing, with the thrift and bill lying on top of it. The machinery shows two steps of gearing. The bottom of the brake-wheel engages the wallower on the upright shaft, and the spur-wheel just below it is in mesh with the stone nut to the left, on its short quant. The bell alarm is worked by a spar snagging on the wallower as it rotates.

New Mill was moved from Ufford to Worlingworth in 1848 and was working up to the 1939–45 war, but was demolished in 1952.

Stone furniture, Trader Mill, Sibsey, Lincolnshire

Pencil, 380mm x 550mm

Fig 84

Here is a clear drawing of the furniture associated with the millstones in a windmill of late date. The stones are over-driven, with a long quant running down from the stone nut above. The tun is circular, the front legs of the horse are of iron, and the whole arrangement is of fairly light construction, with a very functional appearance. The crook string, which passes over the edge of the tun, usually controls the inclination of the shoe. In this case, however, the slope of the shoe is constant, and the string controls the feed of grain by operating a small gate in the bottom of the hopper. The shoe, feeding the grain into the eye of the stone, is to a local pattern. It is shaken by the quant, being held against it by the tension in a horizontal cord provided by the miller's wand to the left-hand side.

Trader Mill is a very fine large tower mill, built in 1877 by Saunderson of Louth, and powered by six sails. It worked until 1954 before becoming derelict, but has been repaired. It is working again and is opened to the public.

Fig 85

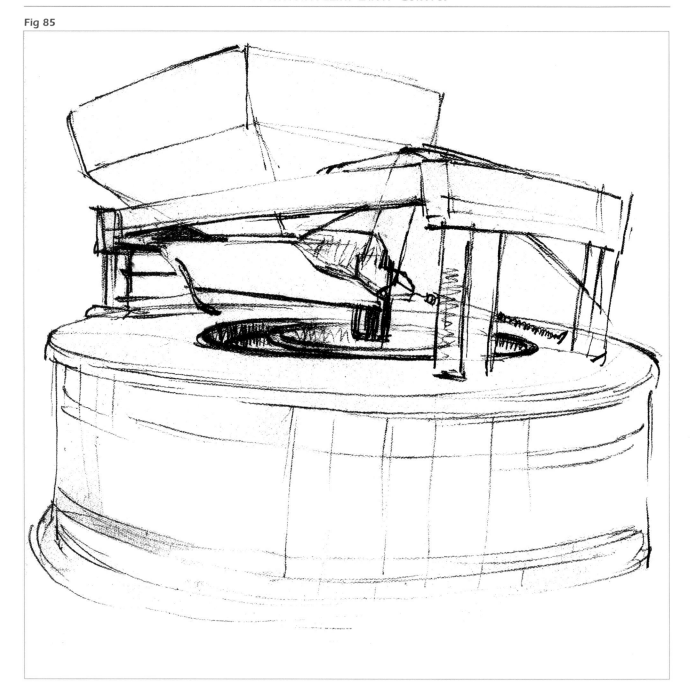

Stone furniture, Ashton Mill, Chapel Allerton, Somerset

Pencil, 255mm x 355mm

The circular tun, the stocky horse supporting the hopper feeding the grain into the shaking shoe – all these elements are of wood, robustly constructed, with a certain rustic quality. At this time the stones had been out of use for a couple of years – replaced by an engine-driven "Dreadnought" mill at a nearby farm. Even when the sketch was made, probably in the early 1920s, this stone furniture was the only set remaining in a windmill in Somerset.

Ashton Mill ceased work in the 1920s, but was restored in 1958 and is now opened to the public. (For this mill see also Figs. 12, 79, 80 & 101.)

Fig 86

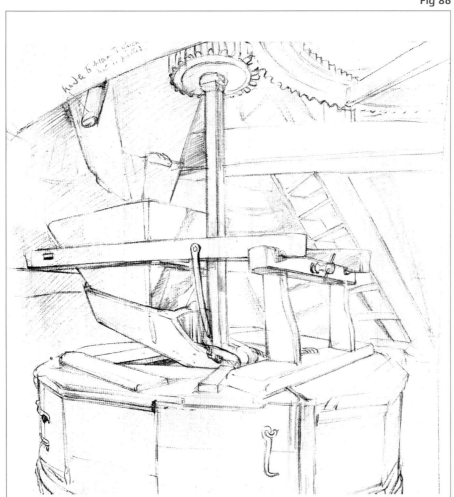

Stone furniture, Melin Mechell, Mynydd Mechell, Anglesey

Pencil, 318mm x 318mm

Another detailed illustration shows over-driven stones, this time with all wooden stone furniture. It is unusual for the miller's wand, the wooden spring that maintains pressure of the shoe against the quant, to be vertical as shown here (attached to the horse, immediately to the left of the quant). Another less common feature is for the twist peg, for altering the angle of slope of the shoe, to be on the end of the horse. This is more commonly on the floor below, where the fineness of the meal can be gauged, and the necessary adjustment made. The iron teeth of the spur-wheel continue up onto the upper face of the wheel, where they would have meshed with the cogs or teeth of a pinion on a horizontal shaft. This extra dimension of tooth was to drive ancillary machinery, and it was a feature of spur-wheels in some parts of Wales.

Thomas Hennell recorded a few details beside his drawing, and, since none of the working parts remain now, these are worth repeating. He noted that there was a "round tapered iron windshaft" with a brake-wheel "of wood, with outer part rounded", and with a segmental cast-iron toothed ring bolted onto it. The wheel had an "iron band-brake". There was a toothed "iron curb on wooden pieces". "The head of the mill turns on them by means of a Y-wheel, twice geared down." There were three pairs of stones and a "flour machine (nut permanently in gear)".

Melin Mechell ceased work about the beginning of the First World War and, despite the completeness of its interior, was in a state of advanced dereliction by the time this drawing was made. It was finally gutted and converted to a dwelling in the late 1970s.

One or two items were found on site by the purchasers of the converted mill, and these have gone to the nearby Llynon Mill, Llanddeusant.

Fig 87

Stone furniture, Tacumshin Mill, Co. Wexford, Ireland

Pencil, 322mm x 414mm

This set of stone furniture is fairly basic, and all of wood. The stones are under-driven, in an octagonal tun, with a damsel agitating the shoe, which in this case appears to be made as a combined unit with the hopper. The two would normally be separate, with the shoe moving independently. As this is probably a fairly early drawing, this feature could be an error of interpretation. The crook string passes over the horse and down through a hole in the floor in the conventional way, but the rope attachment running up to the joists of the bin floor is unusual.

The mill dates from 1846, and its two pairs of stones went out of use in 1908. The reason for some apparent eccentricities may be because parts from a windmill at Ballyfane were used when Tacumshin Mill was restored to commercial use in about 1930. In its present form it only worked for about six years, although a small amount of engine-powered provender milling continued to be carried out in an adjoining building. The mill was restored in 1952 and can be visited by the public. (For this mill see also Figs. 11, 50 & 51.)

Stone furniture, Polegate Mill, East Sussex

Pencil, 480mm x 310mm (with Fig. 118)

Fig 88

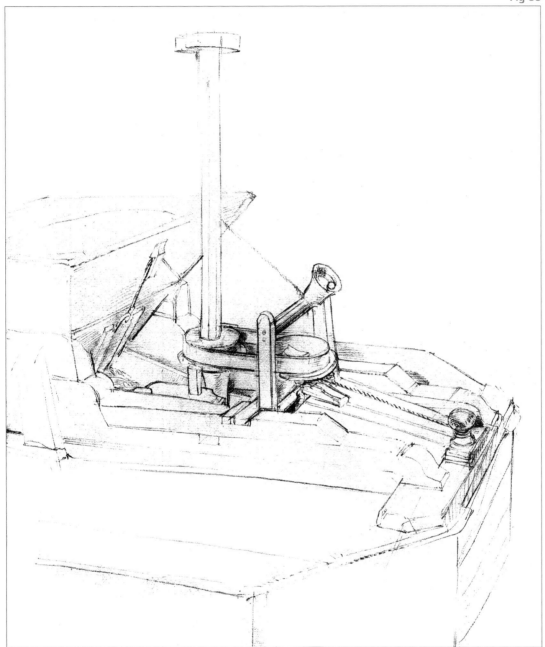

A detailed drawing shows a most unusual variation of stone furniture at Polegate Mill. The stones are over-driven but, instead of the shoe being shaken by the quant in the usual way, there is a special little belt drive to a separate damsel which imparts the shaking motion. The octagonal wooden tun carries a low form of horse to support the hopper. In the front of the hopper is a cord-controlled gate regulating the feed of grain into the shoe. The angle of the shoe is controlled by the crook string, any adjustment being made by the twist peg to the right-hand side. The bell alarm is shown in the working position with the bell raised, tension on the cord being maintained by the weight of grain depressing a leather strap bridging the lower part of the hopper (see Fig. 90). Once this weight of grain disappears the connection relaxes, the little horizontal shaft turns from the weight of the bell and the alarm bell rings, fouling the belt-wheel just below it.

Polegate Mill, also known as Mockett's or Ovenden's Mill, from millers who worked there, is a brick tower mill. It was built with two pairs of over-driven stones, but a third pair was added in 1862. Built in 1817, the mill ceased working by wind in 1942, was restored in 1967, and is now opened to the public.

Fig 89

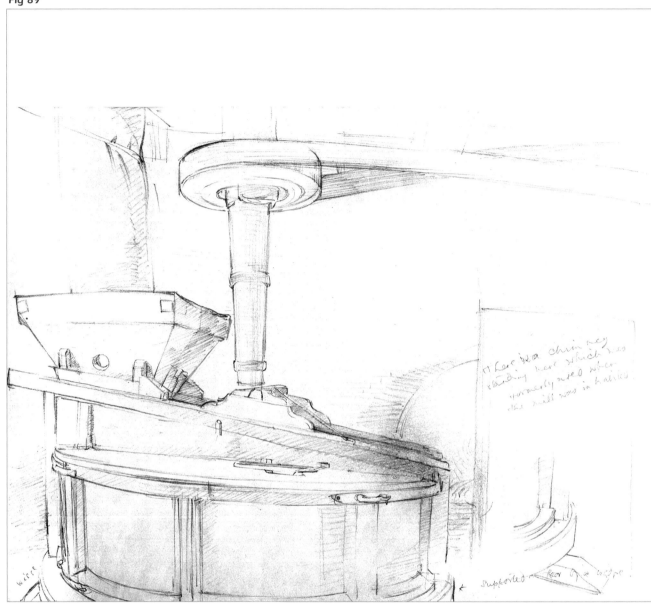

Stone furniture in an unidentified mill

Pencil, 324mm x 412mm

Unfortunately there are few clues to where this was drawn. The stones appear to be over-driven, from a massive, belt-driven shaft acting as a quant. Is this in a windmill or a watermill? The inclination of the belts suggests that the drive was coming from a lay-shaft off to the right. Unfortunately the connection below the bottom of the upright shaft has been omitted from the drawing. The fitting of the hopper to the horse, the carefully cut circular opening in the side of the hopper, the inclined and panelled horse, the construction of the tun including the insertion of wedges under it, the form of upright shaft with the wooden belt-pulley – all these point to this mill not being in the British Isles, but perhaps somewhere in northern continental Europe.

Fig 90

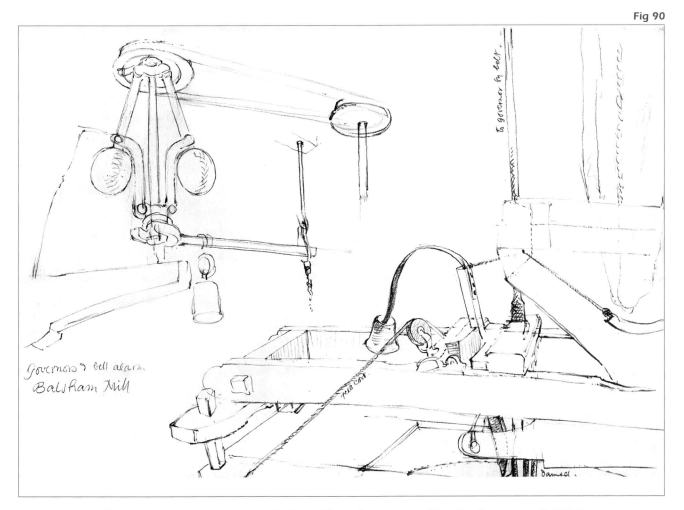

Governors and bell alarm, Balsham Mill, Cambridgeshire

Pencil, 255mm x 378mm

This composite sketch is in complete contrast to the previous drawing. It shows arrangements of bell alarm and governors which are both typical of south-east England. The bell alarm is shown in the ringing position – with no grain depressing the wide leather strap in the "see-through" hopper. This has caused the bell's cruciform wooden frame to pivot on bearings on the horse, throwing the spring-mounted bell to the left, and the bottom end of the frame to the right – where it would be kept moving by the rotation of the damsel. The damsel is a wrought-iron extension of the stone spindle, and is visible at the bottom of the sketch. The inclination of the shoe is controlled by the crook string (here labelled "feed cord") which passes over a little pulley towards the twist peg (below the drawing) for adjustment.

The pair of governors is worked by a belt from the stone spindle below this underdriven pair of millstones. As the rotation speed increases, the balls of the governor swing out in a wider arc by centrifugal force, which raises the linkage. Through a carefully balanced lever, this lowers the runner stone relative to the fixed bedstone, thus narrowing the gap and maintaining an evenly ground product. An example showing how the linkage is arranged to control the tentering is shown in Fig. 92.

Balsham Mill was a smock mill dating from 1831 that had ceased work before Tom Hennell saw it. It has long been demolished.

Belt-driven governors, Thurston Mill, Suffolk

Ink (from a photograph by Rex Wailes), 155mm x 200mm

Fig 91

Here is another drawing of governors, belt-driven from, and below, one of the pairs of stones in a post mill. These governors act in the same way as the last example, although here the linkage they actuated is above them, instead of below.

Thurston Mill dated from about 1750, although this is reputed to have been when it was moved here from Pakenham. It had become derelict before the 1939–45 war and was demolished in about 1953. (For this mill see also Fig. 4.)

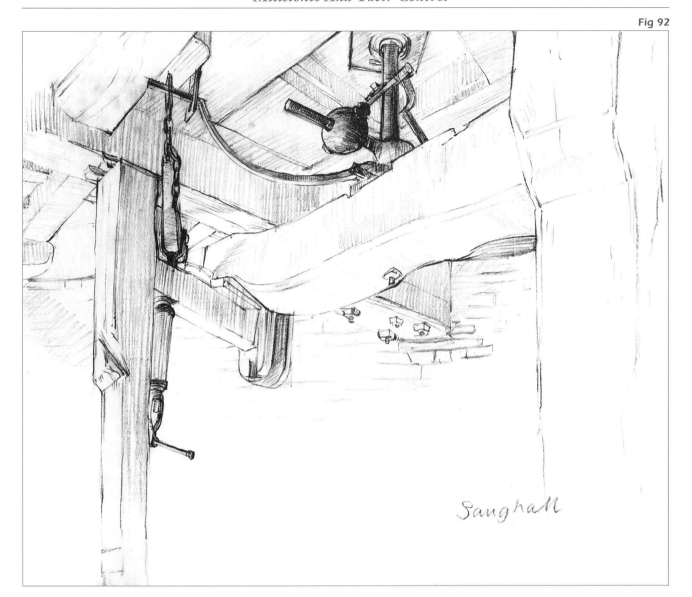

Saughall

Governors and linkage to bridge tree, Gibbet Mill, Saughall, Cheshire

Pencil, 280mm x 380mm

This drawing demonstrates clearly how the governors control the tentering – the adjustment of the gap between the millstones. This pair of stones is over-driven; the spindle seen here is purely to support the runner stone and to make tentering possible. In this case the governors are located on the stone-spindle and, as the speed increases, the balls slide outwards along the bar, lifting it, and the right-hand end of the curved iron linkage-lever, at the same time. The fulcrum is the iron strap, fixed to a timber, so that the left-hand end of the linkage-lever drops a fraction. This has a suspended connection supporting the brayer – the short horizontal beam on the left-hand side. As the brayer is lowered, it acts as another lever and lowers the bridge tree, on which is fixed the footstep bearing of the stone-spindle. The whole spindle is thus lowered fractionally, and the runner stone – which is supported by the spindle – is brought down closer to the fixed bedstone. This movement will tend to grind slightly finer, creating more friction, so that the speed will be reduced. The balls of the governor will then drop, thus reversing the preceding operation. In fact, the effects are more subtle movements of compensation, maintaining a consistent product despite irregularities in the wind power.

There were four pairs of over-driven stones at this mill, which was modified in about 1900, but had ceased working by wind by 1910. Despite a fire in 1927, caused by a gale starting the braked sails, an oil engine drove vertical stones until about 1930. By the 1950s the mill was derelict, and many of the working parts were falling within the tower, which, in the early 1970s, was converted into a dwelling.

Fig 93

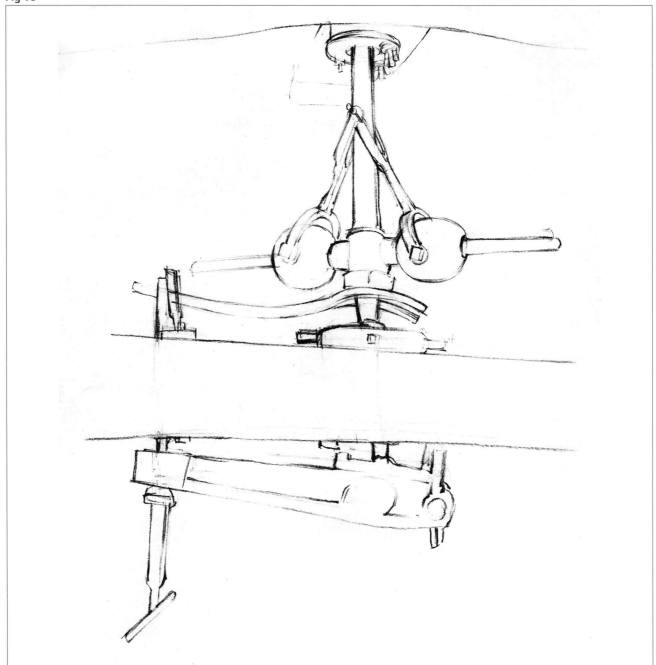

Governors and linkage, Treales Mill, Lancashire

Pencil, 380mm x 280mm

As in the previous example, as they rotate faster, the balls of the governor move outwards and upwards. Here they slide outwards on two iron rods, lifting the rods and linkage-lever together. This is a more compact form of linkage, connected directly to the footstep bearing of the stone-spindle. The fulcrum is fixed to the top of the bridge tree, and the left-hand end of the linkage-lever is connected to the tentering lever beneath the bridge tree. The bridge tree is a fixed one. The tentering lever raises and lowers the footstep bearing of the spindle, and can be controlled either by hand, or automatically via the governors. This was a modification, and is a later variation of the method seen in the previous illustration, having the advantage of maintaining the verticality of the spindle. This over-driven set of stones was one of five pairs.

Treales Mill, an 18th-century tower mill, worked until 1922. It was gutted in the 1950s and was converted to a dwelling in 1960. (For this mill see also Figs. 77 & 78.)

Fig 94

Governors on stone spindle, Parham Mill, Suffolk

Ink (from a photograph by Rex Wailes), 240mm x 210mm

As the governor balls rise, they lift a collar with a double-flanged attachment below it. The raising of this collar on the spindle causes the lever in the linkage arm to the right to lift. The spindle passes up through the eye of the bedstone to support the over-driven runner stone above. Below the governors is the footstep bearing of the spindle, showing the screws by which adjustment is made if the spindle is not vertical. The square cast-iron plate around the eye of the bedstone suggests that the stone is a French burr, probably manufactured by Hughes & Sons of Dover Road, London.

Parham Mill was a post mill, working until the Second World War, but it was demolished in 1944.

The stone floor, Clifton Mill, Lancashire

Pencil, 385mm x 560mm

Fig 95

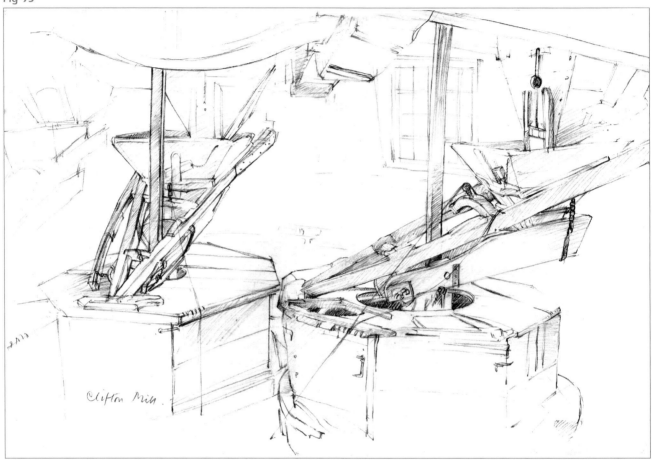

Clifton Mill.

An impressive view of the stone floor of a once fine Lancashire tower mill demonstrates how different local traditions can be. The horses are at a rakish angle, suspended at their upper end. Even the miller's wand, which gives the spring-loading to the shaking shoe, and is seen to the left of the left-hand horse, conforms to this angle. The crook string, for altering the angle of the very large shaking shoe, is clearly seen, running over a tiny pulley and passing through a groove in the edge of the tun, before dropping through a small hole in the floorboards to the twist peg on the floor below. A third set of stone furniture is visible on the left-hand margin of the drawing. The stones are over-driven, with long, heavy, square-section quants. The tuns here have small hooks to enable them to be opened.

Hennell recorded that there were once five pairs of stones, but one pair had been dismantled. In addition, there were two dressing machines, a smutter, and two other machines. Some of the extra ancillary machinery and equipment was because the mill had been producing oatmeal as well as grinding wheat. All these working parts were about to be removed as the mill was to become merely a landscape feature. Clifton mill used to be a fine, five-storeyed tower mill of rendered brick, with a granary and a kiln, but, in about 1970, the complex was redeveloped as a restaurant with accommodation. All that remain of the working parts are the windshaft and striking gear.

Fig 96

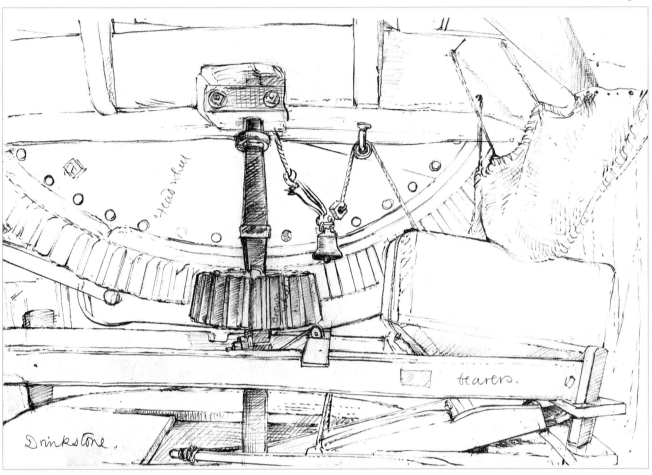

Head wheel and stones, Drinkstone Post Mill, Suffolk

Pencil, 255mm x 380mm

In contrast, this is a detailed drawing showing the drive to the pair of stones in the head of a small post mill, where space is at a premium. The iron stone nut is driven direct off the wooden brake-wheel, or head-wheel. The quant is very short, extending up to the glut box, or top bearing, in the beam above, and with the stone nut only just clearing the top of the wooden horse. The hopper, shoe and miller's wand are clearly visible, as is the bell alarm. As soon as the weight of grain on the leather strap in the hopper is relieved, the weight of the bell – with its additional nut to give it a little extra – is sufficient for the bell to drop into contact with the teeth of the stone nut and ring a warning.

The post mill is dated 1689, and is the oldest in the county, although it has been altered considerably over the years. For over two centuries it belonged to the Clovers, a celebrated milling family, and was run in conjunction with the nearby smock mill. Drinkstone Post Mill has been disused since the early 1970s, but remains complete.

Fig 97

Spur-wheel and millstones, Union Mill, Cranbrook, Kent

Ink, 470mm x 470mm

A good impression of part of the stone floor in a large smock mill is given by this drawing, with the cant posts and weatherboarded walls in the background. The millstones in the foreground are inside an octagonal wooden tun, with the quant bringing the drive to them from the large iron spur-wheel with its wooden cogs at the top of the picture. Immediately below the spur-wheel is another, bevelled iron wheel for driving ancillary machinery via the lay-shaft in the background. Hennell noted the belt drive here as having powered a bolter, for dressing the meal into flour. This drawing appeared in *The Countryman at Work*.

There are three pairs of stones in this fine mill, built in 1814, and working commercially until the 1950s. It is still complete and is opened to the public.

(For this mill see also Frontispiece and Figs. 31, 32, 76 & 116.)

Chapter 6

Sack-hoists

Apart from the actual process of grinding, the hoisting of sacks of grain has long been a very important mechanised operation in a windmill. In primitive mills the single pair of stones was at the top of the structure. In a post mill the arrangement of hoisting was less straightforward, but just as labour-saving. As mills became more powerful, the hoisting of grain became a more important task. Not only did the height of mills increase, but so did the tonnage of grain being ground.

In most windmills a long chain was wound up on a windlass, the sack of grain being attached to it by passing the last foot of chain through the ring on the end, as a running noose, imprisoning the neck of the sack.

As the sack reached each floor it nudged open a pair of hinged sack-traps, which would close again under their own weight as soon as the bulky sack had passed through. At the mid-point of the free edge of these sack-traps was a hole, large enough for the chain to pass through as it unwound under its own weight, falling to the bottom in readiness for the next sackload.

With continual use, every link of a sack-hoist chain achieves a brilliant, mirror finish, reducing friction to a minimum. This aids smooth and fast action, cutting the precious time taken for the length to reach the bottom again. A glistening silver chain is one of the most evocative features of any mill which is still in regular work.

Sack-hoist, Staining Mill, near Blackpool, Lancashire

Pencil, 560mm x 380mm

Fig 98

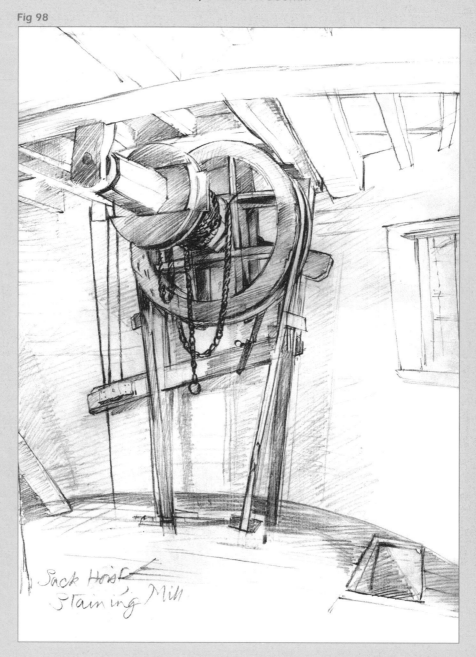

This is an impressive drawing of a fine wooden sack-hoist with its clasp-armed belt-wheel. The belt is tightened by pulling down the rope that disappears through the floor to the left. The end of this rope is attached to a timber at the top of the drawing and, because the rope has passed over two separate pulleys, mechanical advantage is gained, and the left-hand end of the inclined beam below the belt-wheel can be raised with relative ease. As this beam lifts, it acts as a lever, pivoted at the right-hand end, raising a second strut (visible below the belt-wheel) which raises the right-hand end of the beam supporting the far end of the sack-hoist shaft. This tightens the belt connection with a rotating belt-wheel on the floor below, thus setting the hoist in motion and winding in the chain. The effect of this complex leverage is that a relatively easy pull on the rope is sufficient for a heavy sack to be lifted without any slipping of the belt.

Staining Mill is an 18th-century brick tower mill which was gutted by fire in November 1981, only the windshaft surviving. It was converted to a dwelling in the following year. (For this mill see also Fig. 24.)

Fig 99

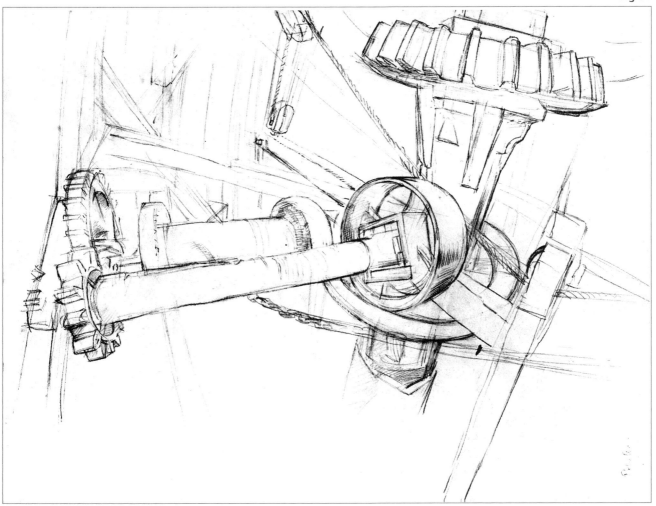

Sack-hoist drive, Preston's Mill, Seaton Ross, East Yorkshire

Pencil, 324mm x 430mm

This accomplished drawing shows the wooden upright shaft with the iron wallower at the top, and, a little below it, a friction ring. The rope in the upper part of the picture controls the position of a wooden beam, on which rests the right-hand end of the lay-shaft in the foreground. When this beam is lowered, the iron wheel on the right-hand end of this lay-shaft is able to roll around on the friction ring, the great weight of the wheel and its shaft holding it in gear. When the friction drive is engaged, the spur gears on the left convey the power to the sack-hoist bollard with its chain behind the lay-shaft, and a sack of grain is then hoisted.

One of the last mills in the county to work by wind, and in commercial use until the end, Preston's Mill was stripped out in 1951. (For this mill see also Figs. 43, 44 & 45.)

Sack tackle, Elmer's Mill, Woolpit, Suffolk

Pencil, 255mm x 380mm

Fig 100

Sack Tackle
Woolpit Mill, Suffolk.

Looking forwards along the ridge of the buck of this very old post mill, this shows the sack-hoist chain being wound around the windlass in the foreground, after passing over the roller on the left-hand side. The belt drive to the hoist is taken from a pulley on the windshaft in front of the brake-wheel. The top of the brake-wheel, with the wooden brake around it, is clearly seen. The wheels to the left of the hoist windlass are part of the engaging mechanism. In this there are two, repeated, steps where a larger wheel is being rotated, winding up a rope or strap on a windlass of smaller diameter. This gives great mechanical advantage, enabling a relatively easy pull of a certain length to have significantly increased lifting power over a shorter distance. Through this complicated linkage, a downward pull on the cord shown in the bottom left-hand corner is converted to a powerful lift on the left-hand end of the wooden beam supporting the far end of the sack-hoist. This tightens the belt, sets the hoisting windlass in motion, and the sack is pulled up through the sack-traps in the floor.

Elmer's Mill was still at work when the drawing was made, but the structure collapsed in 1963.

Fig 101

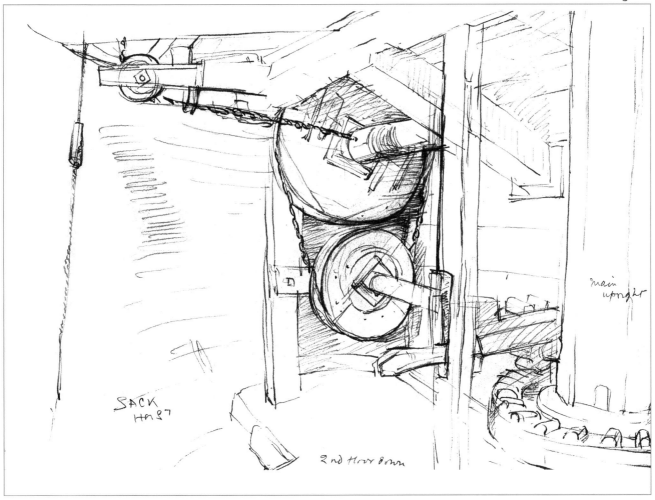

Crown-wheel and sack-hoist, Ashton Mill, Chapel Allerton, Somerset

Pencil, 255mm x 355mm

The wooden upright shaft, with the crown-wheel on it, is on the right-hand side of the picture. The horizontal lever in the foreground, when lowered, allows the pinion to engage the cogs on the crown-wheel. This causes the lower of the two wooden chain-wheels in the background to turn. Normally the chain connecting the two wheels hangs slack, just below the lower wheel. By pulling downwards the cord at the left of the drawing, another lever raises the far end of the upper shaft, thus tightening the chain, so that the upper wheel begins to turn. The upper shaft then acts as a windlass, winding in the hoisting chain. The chain passes over the pulley at the top left, runs up and over another pulley higher up the mill, and then descends the full distance to ground level, for hoisting the sacks through trap-doors in the floors.

Ashton Mill ceased work in the 1920s, but was restored in 1958 and is now opened to the public. (For this mill see also Figs. 12, 79, 80 & 85.)

Fig 102

Sack-hoist, Rath Mill, Co. Wexford, Ireland

Pencil, 303mm x 384mm

This old tower windmill was engine-driven at the time of Hennell's visit. It still retained its thatched cap, although the sails had been removed, and it had been re-floored and re-equipped. An engine house had been erected against the mill tower. The joint in the belt is so prominent and detailed that it is unlikely to have been turning while the drawing was in progress! The drive to the sack-hoist came from the floor below by the vertical belt shown, connected to a rather eccentric iron lay-shaft disappearing to the left. Could this possibly be a re-used crankshaft? It seems that the rope in the foreground pulls down the wooden lever, which raises the beam supporting the vertical belt-wheel, thus tightening the sack-hoist drive-belt from below. The beam in the right foreground appears to be a fixed bridge tree, complete with footstep bearing, so the belt-driven vertical shaft must have been a stone-spindle. Beneath the bridge tree, directly below the footstep bearing, is written "screw". This is assumed to have been a tentering mechanism – similar to the ones shown in Fig. 72.

A smaller belt-wheel on the spindle, immediately above the main belt-wheel, has a horizontal belt connecting it with another vertical shaft on the extreme left-hand side. This shaft is labelled "spindle of sieve", and passes through to the floor below, where it must have driven some sort of dressing machine.

Rath Mill is in Rath townland, near Duncormick, between Wexford and Waterford. Only the gutted shell of the tower remains. (For this mill see also Fig. 9.)

Fig 103

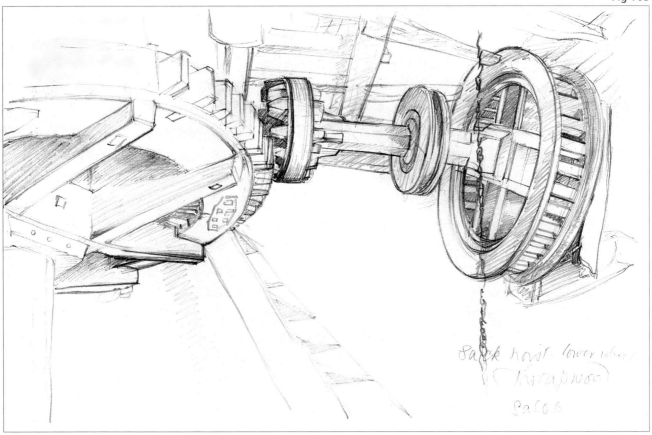

Sack-hoist drive, Bevan's Mill, Threapwood, Cheshire

Pencil, 237mm x 368mm

On the left is a stoutly constructed clasp-armed spur-wheel on the upright shaft. To the right is a lay-shaft with a pinion and two belt-wheels, all of wood. The pinion is shown as a face gear and it is not clear how it was driven. In a face gear it is normally the larger of the two wheels which has the cogs on the face of the wheel, not the smaller. A small face-geared pinion like this could not have meshed with the cogs on the periphery of the spur-wheel. Was there another set of cogs or teeth on the upper side of the spur-wheel, as was the case in some mills further west? If so, there is no sign of it in the drawing. It remains a puzzle. Presumably the clasp-armed belt-wheel to the right was the one which powered the sack-hoist further up the mill, but the absence of a drive-belt on it shows it was no longer in use.

At the time, Hennell noted the mill as being derelict and without its cap, having not worked for about 50 years. Probably dating from the late 18th century, the machinery was all of wood, and two of the three pairs of over-driven stones were then still in place. Bevan's Mill ceased working commercially in the 1880s. It has remained derelict ever since and, although the three-storeyed brick tower still stands, what remain of the working parts are now all in a heap in the bottom.

117

Sack-hoist drive, Coleby Heath Mill, Coleby, Lincolnshire

Pencil, 563mm x 384mm

Fig 104

This is only a rough sketch, but it appears to show the rope-operated lever to the right, which raises the nearer end of the wooden beam supporting the lay-shaft. As this beam is lifted the belt over the belt-pulley on the left is tightened and the hoisting chain is wound onto the drum to the right. The lay-shaft, belt-pulley and hoisting drum had been part of a large restoration programme, including the replacement, in iron, of the cap and the fan supports. Despite the modern appearance of the machinery in this drawing, the work was carried out by Ruston of Lincoln following a fire as early as 1863.

Coleby Heath Mill was a tall tower mill with six sails. It was too close to the airfield, however, and was reduced to a stump in 1942. Now even that has gone.

Chapter 7

Other Machines

As corn-grinding windmills became larger and more powerful, the wind was used to power all sorts of ancillary machines. These included cleaners for the grain, dressers of various types to remove the bran from the meal to yield white flour, and a very wide assortment of other labour-saving devices. In tower mills and smock mills these could normally be incorporated within the structure of the mill. However, in post mills there was usually insufficient room, requiring the addition of small extensions to the buck, usually at the rear, with an inserted link from the main machinery to drive the machine in question.

Those illustrated here are a few machines which caught Tom Hennell's eye.

Smutter, Hoyle's Mill, Alford, Lincolnshire

Pencil, 560mm x 380mm

Fig 105

A rather grand cleaning machine is shown, apparently driven by a lay-shaft from the crown-wheel. The cleaner, or "smutter" as it is labelled here, comprises a wire machine above, and a winnower below. The wire machine consists of an inclined tube of wire mesh, supported by a circular wooden frame. Within the tube is a shaft running the whole length, equipped with a series of brushes or beaters. The grain was fed into the upper end of this tube while the brushes were revolving at high speed. Any dust and fungal growth passed through the mesh and originally was blown off through wooden trunking and out of the window by the fan. In the picture the pinion from the crown-wheel has been taken out of gear by dropping the beam supporting that end of the lay-shaft to the cleaner. A wire machine can function as a method of cleaning grain or of dressing meal, depending on the mesh size.

Hoyle's Mill has five sails and was built by Oxley of Alford in about 1837. It is still at work and is opened to the public. This machine still survives.

Fig 106

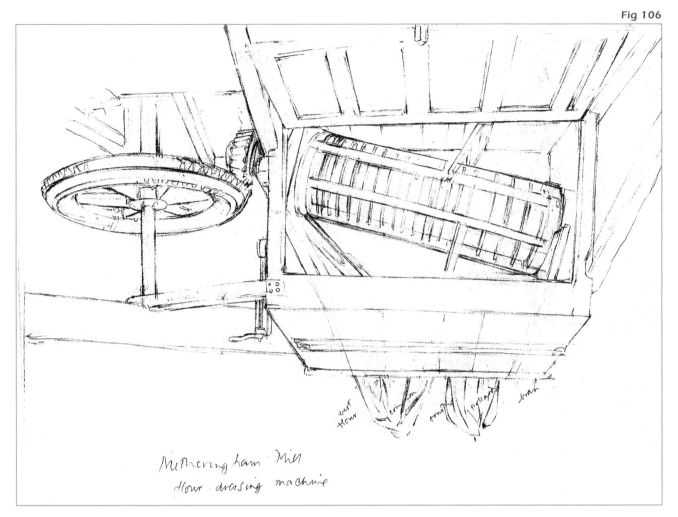

Flour dressing machine, Metheringham Mill, Lincolnshire

Pencil, 280mm x 385mm

This drawing shows a more conventional wire machine for dressing the meal after it is ground. It is essentially the same as the upper part of the machine in the previous illustration, except that in this case the mesh of the wire gauze forming the drum would be much finer. The size of this mesh becomes coarser in stages, from left to right, so the finest flour falls through into the first compartment, with coarser products following, and the bran drops out at the end of the drum. Each of the products falls into a separate chute and is bagged up below. At the top of the drawing can be seen the raised side panel to the machine. When operating, this has to be kept shut, as the internal brushes rotate at very high speed and would generate an enormous quantity of dust.

Metheringham Mill was a tall, six-sailed tower mill with four pairs of stones, and was built in 1867. Already derelict when Thomas Hennell saw it, it has remained so ever since.

The "jumper", Friston Mill, Suffolk

Ink (from a photograph by Rex Wailes), 240mm x 280mm

Fig 107

Another view in this powerful post mill shows the "jumper", or mechanical sieve, in the tail of the mill, on the meal floor. It acted as a primitive dressing machine, sieving the meal immediately after it had come from the pair of stones driven off the tail-wheel. Rex Wailes records that this machine was driven by a lever connection from an iron skew gear bolted onto the windshaft in front of the tail-wheel. At the top of the drawing can be seen the spur-wheel which drove the third pair of stones in the tail of the mill.

Friston Mill dates from 1812 and boasts a three-storeyed roundhouse and three pairs of stones. It ceased work by wind in about 1959 and, despite coming very close to being demolished on a couple of occasions, it is still standing. (For the two pairs of stones in the head of this mill see Fig. 66.)

Fig 108

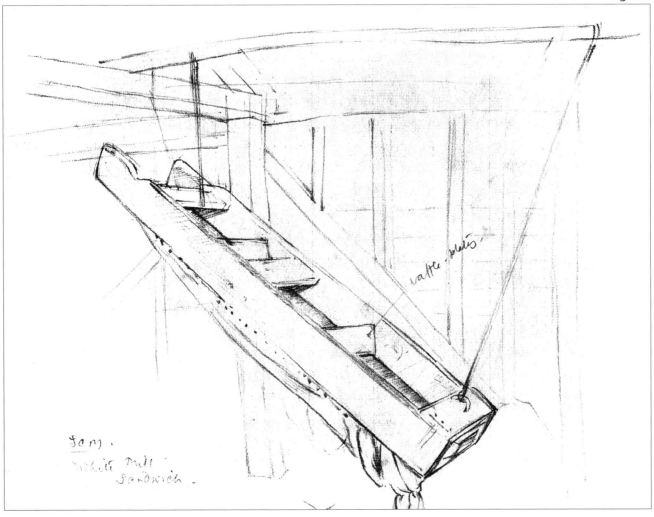

Scry, White Mill, Sandwich, Kent

Pencil, 240mm x 314mm

This is a sieve for removing dust from wheat that is destined for flour. The scry was suspended from the floor above and acted as a chute from bin to hopper. As the grain slid down the slope it was spread by loose baffle plates, and contact between wheat and mesh was maintained. At the bottom the clean grain discharged through the small rectangular aperture into an ingenious balance mechanism in the hopper, triggered by the weight of corn on it, which opened and shut a small trap-door in the spout between bin and scry automatically. Any dust falling through the mesh was caught by a suspended canvas sleeve, and was bagged off separately. Such pieces of equipment were often to be found, but they went out of use generally in the First World War, when so many mills stopped producing flour and turned to animal feeds. A scry is now a rarity, but this one still survives.

White Mill is a smock mill with two pairs of stones, built in about 1760. It worked by wind until about 1926, although milling continued until 1957, powered by an engine. White Mill is complete and well maintained, and is opened to visitors.

Fig 109

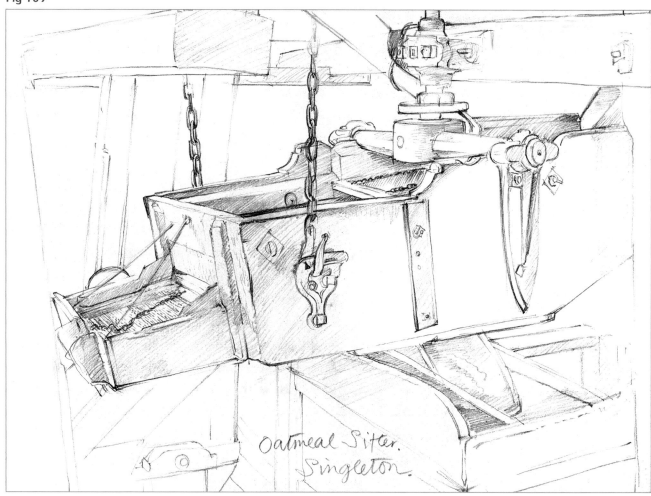

Oatmeal sifter, Singleton Mill, Lancashire

Pencil, 280mm x 385mm

Few mills now contain any machinery or equipment associated with oatmeal, although this was once a product of a significant number of windmills in northern England. The constructional details and embellishments of a§ mechanical sieve for oatmeal are well seen in this excellent drawing. The machine stood on the ground floor, worked by an eccentric gear on the iron shaft coming down from the floor above. The whole unit would rock sharply in a circular movement, constrained by the hanging chains. The oatmeal was fed into the machine by two meal-spouts, presumably from two pairs of stones. The oversize passed over the mesh and was discarded at the left-hand end into a bin below. The finer meal passed through the mesh and fell into a separate bin to the right.

Singleton Mill was a tower mill which ceased to work by wind in 1916. After that it was powered by an oil engine. This changeover involved removing the upright shaft and conventional gears, and replacing them with belt-drives connecting the engine to the stones. Eventually the mill was pulled down by a traction engine in 1956 to make way for a house.

Groat machine, Marton Mill, Little Marton, Lancashire
Pencil, 380mm x 560mm

Fig 110

Groat Machine

At another northern oatmeal mill is this beautifully drawn example of a machine like a glorified winnower on a farm. It was fitted below the meal-spout of a pair of stones which were set far enough apart to merely crack the oats after they had been dried in a kiln. The fan at the right-hand end blew a strong blast of air through the ducting. The cracked oats were hardly affected by the draught, but the husks, and any dust, were blown away. The clean kernels, or groats, were then hoisted and put through a pair of close-set millstones to produce the oatmeal.

This four-storeyed tower mill of rendered brick was built with four pairs of stones. It replaced a post mill in 1839, worked until 1928, was restored in 1938, the 1960s and the mid-1980s, and is now open by appointment. Part of the restoration work was somewhat controversial, however. Some items were removed, including this particular machine, and the kiln. Of what survives, various mechanical parts are now painted in bright colours.

Moulin Deschodt, Wormhoudt, Nord, France

Ink and watercolour, 505mm x 485mm

Fig 111

This brilliant picture captures the atmosphere of a windmill hard at work, with full cloth on the sails and clouds scudding across the sky. The post mill is impressive, and is a wonderful example of those of the Nord area of northern France. Despite its size and power, however, it does not have the sophistication of its counterparts in eastern England. It has common sails and lacks a fantail, being turned to wind by the long tail-pole. The form of the roof of the buck is a distinctive feature which is quite different from any post mill in England. The reason for this picture being placed in this chapter is to draw attention to the extensions which have been added to the mill. These are to accommodate extra items of ancillary machinery. Not only are there other, similar, additions to the buck which are not visible in this view, but each of the two shown here has even been extended since Thomas Hennell's visit!

Chapter 8
Tools And Equipment

There are various special tools and pieces of equipment which are virtually restricted to mills. They have evolved gradually and become traditional, and many have developed certain regional characteristics.

As would be expected, this was precisely where Hennell was in his element. He noticed, and drew with his simple but flowing style, a few examples of these milling items, conveying something of their simple rustic charm.

Hand Winch for Raising Stones, West Wratting Mill, Cambridgeshire

Pencil, 395mm x 480mm

Fig 112

This is a very attractive drawing which, from its style, probably dates from the early 1920s. It shows a fine example of a very old stone crane, a fixture on the stone-floor in this smock mill. The crane was used to lift the runner stone when the stones needed dressing, or if there was some other problem. A hand-operated crank turned a huge worm, which engaged the spur gear, thus rotating the vertical windlass above and winding in the rope. At the end of the rope is a lewis, a dovetail iron tenon, made in three pieces, for lifting blocks of stone. A spare one hangs on a nail fixed to a cant post in the background. For such an implement to be used, there has to be a suitable hole drilled into the side of the runner stone. The two outer arms of the dismantled lewis are inserted into the hole and the middle arm is then forced between them, tightening their grip. After re-assembling the device, the stone is ready for lifting.

West Wratting Mill is the oldest dated smock mill in England, with 1726 carved on the brakewheel. It ceased work commercially in 1924 and continued to deteriorate until 1957. Since then the mill has been repaired and maintained in good condition in private ownership. (For an external view of the mill see Fig. 41.)

Fig 113

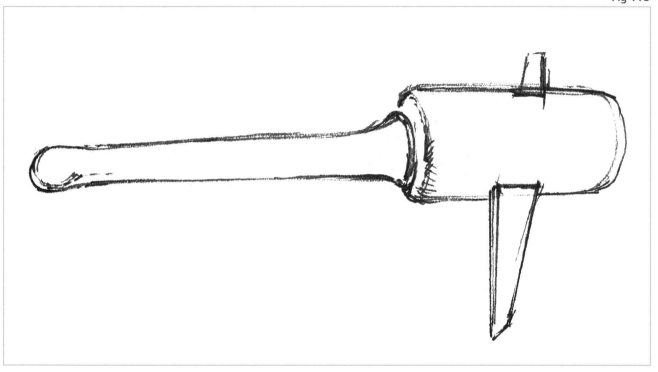

Mill-bill and thrift

Pencil, 255mm x 380mm

The wooden thrift contains a mill-bill with its sharpened ends of tempered steel. This was the traditional tool used by the stone-dresser to cut the furrows in the face of the millstone. The drawing shows how the mortise through the thrift is tapered so that, in use, the bill becomes ever more tightly wedged. The bill is double-ended so it can be reversed when blunted; a slight tap on the other end of the bill will usually loosen it. A series of bills would be prepared, and then used and discarded one by one, as the task progressed. When all the bills had been blunted the whole set would be sharpened again for re-use. Where this thrift and bill were drawn is not recorded.

Stone dressing

Each: Ink, 316mm x 480mm

Fig 114

These two drawings show a stone dresser re-cutting the furrows on a millstone. The stone appears to be a runner that has been laid on its back on blocks. A thrift and bill are being used, two-handed, with a brush close by – so that the working area of the stone can be kept free of dust and chippings. Unfortunately the name of neither man nor mill was specified.

It had been assumed that the scenes were in a windmill, but Thomas Hennell wrote, in a letter to Rex Wailes of August 14th 1942, that he had been lucky enough to record the old miller, Mr. Mettam, of Ollerton Mill, dressing his stones. It is likely, therefore, that these two drawings were done at Ollerton Watermill in Nottinghamshire. The last miller at Ollerton was Frank Mettam, who would have been in his mid-30s in 1942, so these drawings must have been of George Mettam, his father.

Fig 115

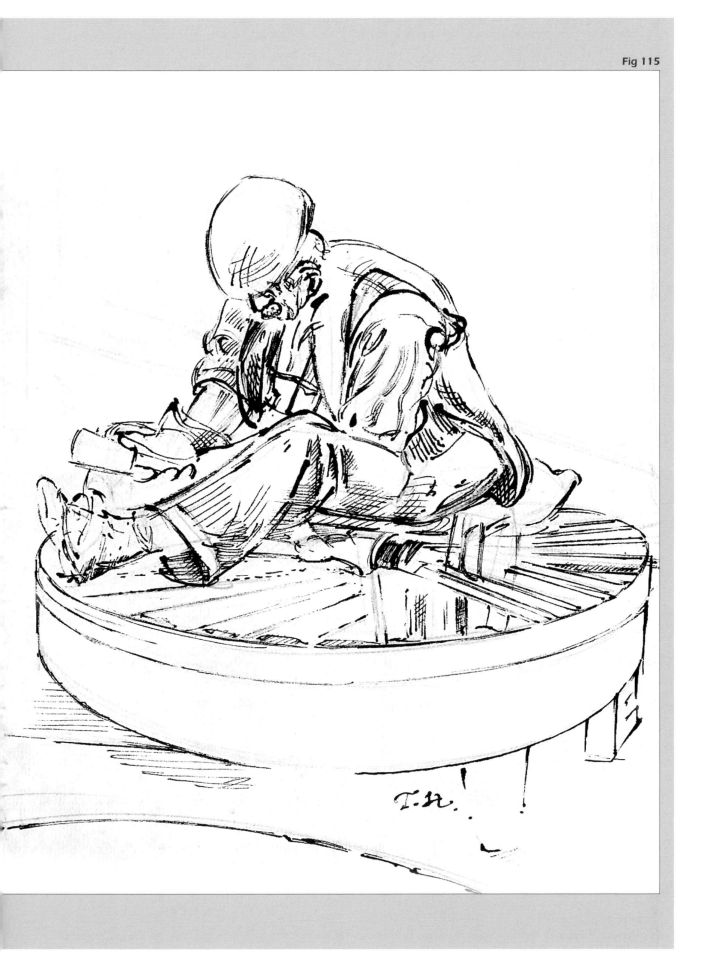

Fig 116

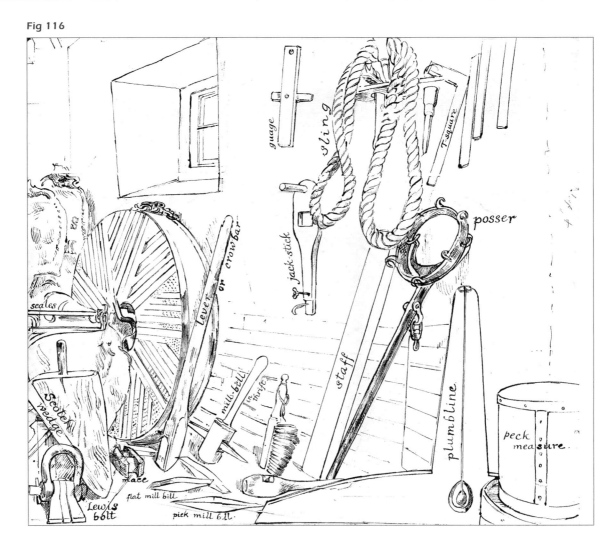

Fig. 116. Milling tools

Ink, 413mm x 477mm

The crowbar is used to lever up the runner stone with care, the lift being then consolidated by inserting the handled wedge into the gap, before levering once again with wooden pads to protect the face of the stone. The runner stone is seen, well-dressed with furrows, and containing in the eye the iron rynd or bridge. On the floor in front is the iron mace. This fits on top of the stone spindle and interlocks with the rynd of the runner stone. The spindle then takes the full weight of the runner, and the mace imparts the rotation to the rynd – and thus to the runner.

At the bottom of the picture is a wooden thrift plus two kinds of mill-bill, with an assembled thrift and bill above, and a brush for sweeping the chippings off the millstone. Before the stone-dressing begins, the staff, or paint-staff, shown to the right of the brush, has raddle, or iron oxide pigment, applied to its face. The staff is then worked over the grinding area of the stone, showing up the high spots, which then have to be brought down to a flat surface before the furrows are cut. Before the runner stone is put back into position, the plumb-line is used to see that the surface of the bedstone is level. The inverted "T" shape of the frame for the plumb-line is very convenient, and the tool can be set down on the stone in various directions as a check. It is after this operation that the jack-stick is used (see caption to Fig. 117). The jack-stick shown hanging on the wall here is very similar to the top one in Fig. 117, which was at Pakenham Mill.

The item labelled "posser" is a tool that can be suspended from a joist by the attachment on the long straight lever-arm, and a sack is hung below from the circle of hooks. By vigorous up and down motion on the end of the lever, the contents of the sack are shaken down, and more can then be added. Such an operation can make a considerable difference when bagging up bran, for instance. (A similar example is seen in Fig. 118.)

This drawing appeared on page 62 of *The Countryman at Work* by Thomas Hennell, and, by inference, was of artefacts at Union Mill, Cranbrook, Kent. (For this mill see also Frontispiece & Figs. 31, 32, 76 & 97.)

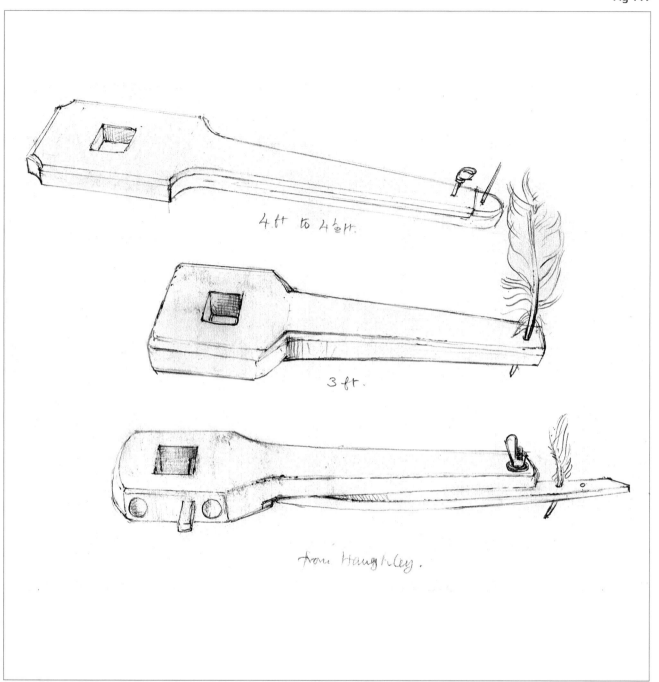

Jack-sticks from Suffolk mills

Pencil, 255mm x 340mm

A jack-stick is to ensure that the spindle is precisely at a right-angle to the surface of the bedstone. It is used before the runner stone is set in its working position, but after making sure the surface of the bedstone is precisely level. The left-hand end of each stick has a square aperture for fitting snugly over the top of the spindle, so that the jack-stick is parallel with the grinding surface of the bedstone. The quill at the right-hand end is then adjusted so that its tip just scratches the stone. As the spindle is rotated, when everything is set up correctly, there will be an even scratching noise all the way round. If not, the four screws on the footstep bearing, at the base of the spindle, need to be adjusted to bring the spindle vertical. The upper two jack-sticks are from Pakenham Mill, Suffolk and are made for millstones of different sizes. The top one has a screw for adjusting the length the quill projects. The third jack-stick is from Haughley Mill, Suffolk, and has not only the adjusting screw, but two positions for the quill, and a wedge for clamping tightly onto the spindle.

"Sack holder from Dicker Mill, now in Polegate Mill", East Sussex

Pencil, 477mm x 311mm

Fig 118

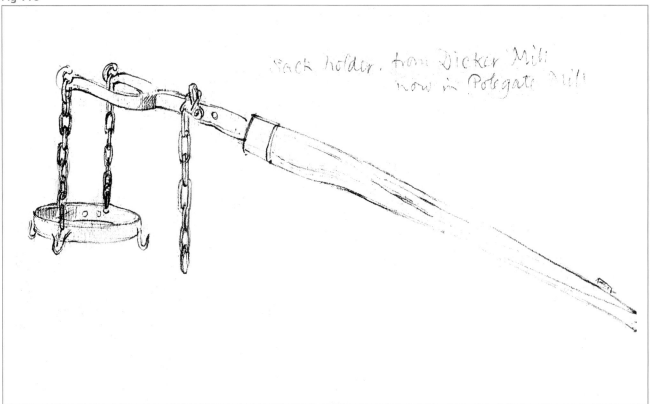

This item is sometimes known as a "posser", and is a more rustic example than the one seen in Fig. 116. It can be suspended by the chain attachment on the long straight lever-arm, and a sack is hung below from the circle of hooks. A vigorous up and down motion on the end of the lever causes settling of the contents of the sack, so that more can then be added, and the operation repeated. For a loose commodity, like bran, this can make a great difference when bagging up.

Of the two windmills formerly at Dicker, it probably came from Lower Dicker New Mill, an early 19th-century post mill that collapsed in 1929.

The Mill Possessed

'Twas a derelict smock-mill, wood-built, weather-boarded and tarred

Longwhile unused, yet not spoiled, nor wholly unfit

Bearings and brakewheel were still, sweeps patched, bolted and barred.

Yet of a sudden one night (none could the riddle resolve)

Groanings and shakings were, as by holdless demon possessed

Up-spin the brazen balls, turns the runner of Derbyshire grit

And sails to quiver begin, the workings to creak and revolve.

Speed-gathering, it seemed the hoppers were filled with grain

And all to kibble the corn, and rub into flour again –

The wormy bolter moves; firsts, bran and middlings dressed

As for two centuries past the old miller's work was up-kept.

Out of the dusty sleeves flows the soft-streaming flour

And like a whirlwind it works, steady-grinding for many an hour.

Next morning, no man was seen, but all neatly bagged-up and swept

Nor any could tell by whom was bought or powdered the grist.

But 'twas an Easter Friday, and millers, remembering Christ

Sometimes set flour apart, or offerings bequeath of bread.

So, 'twas supposed, the spirit returned, through

Some faithful Church-going miller – long dead.

Fig 119

Thomas Hennell

This picture of the artist was thought particularly apt to include here. Not only was it found amongst the papers of the late Rex Wailes, in the form of a photographic print, but it is possibly a self portrait.

A comparison between Thomas Hennell's record and what still stands is a salutary lesson on the vulnerability of our historic windmill heritage. Of the seventy-eight mills illustrated here only twenty-five are still more or less in the same condition today, but even these have suffered to some degree. This may have been from decay, unsympathetic repairs and alterations, or, at best, merely those unsightly notices and barriers engendered by the insatiable demands of "health and safety". What has been lost in many cases is that indefinable sense of "atmosphere".

Twenty-seven of the mills have disappeared completely, and twenty-six have changed dramatically. In this last category are partial demolitions, removal of machinery by accident or by design, and the inevitable domestic conversions. Not all counties have fared equally. Of course this sample of mills is not large enough for proper statistical conclusions to be drawn. However, it is significant that Hennell made drawings at eighteen windmills in Suffolk, one of the richest counties for mills of wooden construction, but of these only four are standing today.

It is the sound, smell and feel of a working mill – the parallel of a working steam engine – that is so evocative. Perhaps we are envious of the opportunities that Hennell had, to savour so many mills in this last period of working, but we must also be grateful for his admirable talent in recording so much of what we have lost for ever.

GLOSSARY OF WINDMILL TERMS

ANNULAR Descriptive of the area between two concentric circles.

BATTER The degree of taper of a windmill tower.

BEDSTONE The lower, fixed, millstone of a pair.

BELL ALARM An alarm bell caused to ring automatically when the supply of grain to the millstones is about to cease.

BEVEL GEAR A gear with its face at an angle; used for turning the drive through 90 degrees.

BILL see Mill-bill

BOLTER A dresser, for separating out the white flour, in which meal is passed down a rotating inclined cloth cylinder, the sieving action aided by external stationary beaters.

BRAKE-WHEEL The main gear-wheel on the windshaft. The brake is clamped tightly around the periphery of the wheel when the mill is stationary or stopping.

BRAYER A horizontal adjustable beam supporting the front end of a bridge tree. This is a feature of older mills.

BREAST That part of a post mill forward of the main post.

BRIDGE The horizontal iron beam supporting the weight of the spindle and runner stone.

BRIDGE TREE The horizontal wooden beam supporting the weight of the spindle and runner stone.

BUCK The body of a post mill, supported by, and turning on, the main post.

CANISTER Cast-iron sockets on the end of the windshaft for the attachment of sails.

CANTS The basic segments making up the curved portion of a wooden gear.

CANT POST The posts running up the corners of a smock mill.

CLASP-ARMED A wheel in which pairs of arms clasp the shaft.

COG A projecting unit on a gear which has been inserted into the wheel; usually made of wood (cf. tooth).

COMMON SAIL A sail which has cloth spread over it when in use.

COMPASS-ARMED A wheel in which the arms are radial, each arm passing through the mortised shaft.

CRANK An arm attached to, and rotated by, a shaft.

CROOK STRING The string for adjusting the slope of the shoe which feeds grain into the millstones.

CROSS A cast-iron fitting on the front of the windshaft to which are bolted the sails on its 4, 5, 6 or 8 arms.

CROSS TREES The horizontal timbers at the base of the main post in a post mill. They support the quarter bars.

CROWN-WHEEL A gear mounted on the upright shaft specifically to drive ancillary machinery.

CURB The track on top of a tower, or smock, mill on which the cap turns to face the wind (see also dead curb and live curb).

DAMSEL An upward extension from the stone-spindle. It agitates the shoe, causing grain to be admitted to the millstones.

DEAD CURB A curb on which the cap frame turns by means of greased blocks or pads only.

DISHED A gear is said to be "dished" when the cogs or teeth are on a different plane from the point where the arms meet the shaft.

DRESSING According to context, either: (a) the separation and grading of the white flour from the coarser particles in the meal; or (b) the cutting of furrows on the grinding face of a millstone.

ECCENTRIC A device in which, by using two circles with different centres, a rotating shaft can impart a rotary motion to a machine.

FACE GEAR A wooden gear turning the drive through 90 degrees with cogs set in the face of the larger wheel. This engages a spur-geared pinion.

FAN-STAGE The platform behind the cap giving access to the fantail.

FANTAIL (OR FAN) A rotary fan with oblique blades for automatically keeping the mill facing the wind.

FOOTSTEP The bottom end of a shaft.

FRENCH BURR A millstone made up of numerous cut blocks of flint-like material, quarried in France but commonly made up into millstones in the country of use.

GLUT-BOX The top bearing for a quant, with a removable locking piece. This either holds the quant in place, or, when the upper part of the quant is moved aside, taking it out of gear, prevents it from returning.

GOVERNORS A means of automatic adjustment of the gap between the millstones when a change in speed occurs.

GRAPPLING IRONS Four eye-bolts which are fitted tightly around a large square-section timber to hold it together when it is under strain.

GROATS Oat grains with their husks removed.

HEAD-WHEEL The front one of a pair of wheels on the windshaft of a post mill, each driving a pair of stones.

HOLLOW POST MILL A post mill driving machinery below by means of an upright shaft running down the centre of the bored-out post which supports the mill.

HORSE The frame standing on the tun and supporting the hopper.

JACK-STICK A stick, with a quill, that locks onto the top of the spindle, for checking that the spindle is vertical.

JOCKEY PULLEY A loose pulley on a swinging arm. Used for tensioning a belt.

JUMPER An inclined sieve with an oscillating movement.

LAY-SHAFT A horizontal shaft.

LEWIS A locking device with three prongs, for lifting a millstone.

LIVE CURB A curb on which the cap frame turns on rollers.

MEAL The product of grinding with millstones, before any separation and grading into constituents is carried out.

MIDDLINGS The portion of meal left when the white flour and the bran have each been removed.

MILL-BILL A reversible steel chisel with tempered blade at each end, for dressing millstones. Fits into a thrift.

MILLER'S WAND A springy length of wood used to maintain tension on the side of the shoe so that it is shaken against the damsel, or quant, regulating the flow of grain to the millstones.

MORTISE WHEEL A gear-wheel with mortises in it to hold wooden cogs. This term is usually applied to a cast-iron wheel.

NECK BEARING The bearing supporting the front end of a windshaft.

OPEN TRESTLE The wooden framework supporting a post mill, where it is exposed, as distinct from being protected by a roundhouse.

OVER-DRIVEN Millstones which are driven from above.

PATENT SAILS Shuttered sails that are self-regulating.

PINION The smaller gear of a pair.

POLL END Cast-iron sockets at the front end of a windshaft for attachment of sails; also known as a canister. This superseded the original sort which was mortised out of timber.

POSSER A lever to which a sack can be attached for the shaking down of the contents.

POST The main post supporting the buck of a post mill, upon which the mill turns to face the wind.

POST MILL A windmill which relies upon a fixed post for its support, the whole mill turning to face the wind.

PROVENDER Animal feed.

QUARTER BARS Inclined timbers in the framework supporting the main post of a post mill. The lower ends rest on the outer ends of the cross trees.

QUANT The iron shaft connecting the runner stone to the stone nut when the stones are over-driven.

RACK A bar of cast iron with a series of teeth on one side to engage a pinion.

ROLLER REEFING SAILS Sails using a non-automatic system of roller-blinds instead of shutters.

ROUNDHOUSE A protective building incorporating the trestle support of a post mill.

RUNNER STONE The upper millstone which rotates over the fixed bedstone.

SACK-TRAPS A pair of hinged doors set in the floor, through which a sack can be hoisted. They close by their own weight immediately the sack has passed through.

SAIL BARS The wooden bars across the sails, mortised into the whips.

SCOOP WHEEL A wheel turned by a windmill for pumping water. It worked like a waterwheel "in reverse", lifting water instead of being driven by it.

SHOE The oscillating tray, shaken by being spring-held against the damsel or quant, feeding corn to the millstones from the hopper.

SHUTTER One of a series of spring-loaded, hinged vanes making up the area of a windmill sail.

SKEW GEAR A pair of engaging gears in which the two shafts are neither parallel nor at 90 degrees.

SMOCK MILL A windmill constructed of wood upon which only the cap is turned to face the wind.

SMUTTER A machine for cleaning grain, particularly to remove smut, or black fungus, from wheat.

SPIDER The couplings radiating from the front end of the striking rod, so called from their fanciful resemblance to a spider's legs.

SPINDLE The vertical iron shaft supporting and turning the runner stone when under-driven. When over-driven, the spindle merely supports the runner.

SPRING SAIL Sail with shutters which are spring-loaded, each sail controlled by one spring; not self-regulating.

SPUR-WHEEL A gear in which the cogs or teeth project radially from the rim.

STAGE A platform around the body of a windmill.

STOCK A length of timber, passing through a canister at its centre, with a sail whip fixed to each projecting length.

STONE CRANE A hand-operated crane for lifting a runner stone off the bedstone.

STONE FURNITURE The fittings associated with millstones, comprising tuns, horses, hoppers, stone cranes and any other related items.

STONE NUT The final pinion in a gear chain in a corn mill. It is mounted on a quant or spindle, depending on whether the stones are over-driven or under-driven.

STRAKES Strips of iron attached to a windlass, or roller, to prevent wear from a hoist chain, and sometimes to increase the effective diameter.

STRIKING CHAIN A chain, hanging at the rear of the mill, by which the shutters on patent sails are controlled.

STRIKING GEAR The mechanism for controlling the angle of the shutters on the sails.

STRIKING LEVER The lever controlling the position of the striking rod.

STRIKING ROD The rod which passes through the length of a bored-out windshaft enabling the shutters on the sails to be controlled from the rear of the mill.

SWEEP The word for a windmill sail used in Kent.

TAIL BEARING The bearing supporting the tail end of a windshaft.

TAIL-POLE The pole protruding from the rear of a post mill, by which the mill is turned to wind.

TAIL-WHEEL The rear one of a pair of wheels on the windshaft of a post mill, each driving millstones. The term is also used for a wheel on the end of a tail-pole to facilitate the turning of the mill to wind.

TAIL-WINDED The result of serious structural and mechanical damage to a windmill caused by strong winds catching the rear of the mill.

TENTERING The altering of the gap between the fixed bedstone and the movable runner stone. This controls the fineness of the meal.

THRIFT The handle into which a mill-bill fits for use in dressing millstones.

TOOTH A projecting unit on an iron gear, cast integrally with the wheel or rack (cf. cog).

TOWER MILL A windmill constructed of stone or brick upon which only the cap is turned to face the wind.

TUN The casing, usually wooden, surrounding a pair of millstones.

TWIST PEG A wooden peg controlling the crook string, which alters the angle of the shoe, and therefore the flow of grain being fed to the stones.

UNDER-DRIVEN Millstones which are driven from below.

WALLOWER The gear wheel at the top of the upright shaft, engaged by the brake-wheel.

WEATHER The twist in a windmill sail to increase the power.

WHIP The main member in a sail, commonly attached to a stock.

WINDLASS A shaft upon which a chain or rope is wound.

WINDSHAFT The shaft conveying the power from the sails into the mill.

WINNOWER A machine for cleaning grain, comprising a fan for blowing off any dust, and sieves for removing any coarse contaminants.

WIRE MACHINE A dresser, for separating out the white flour, in which meal is passed down a stationary inclined wire-mesh cylinder, aided by internal rotating brushes or beaters.

Y-WHEEL A wheel carrying a rope or chain in which the periphery is splayed to give a "Y" in cross section.

This is a list of the main published sources which have been used in the compilation of information for this book:

Apling, Harry, *Norfolk Corn Windmills*, The Norfolk Windmills Trust, 1984.

Batten, M. I., and Smith, Donald, *English Windmills*, The Architectural Press (2 volumes), 1930 & 1932.

Brunnarius, Martin, *The Windmills of Sussex*, Phillimore & Co. Ltd., 1979.

Carley, John M., *The Story of Meopham Mill*, Meopham Publications Committee, 1971.

Coulthard, Alfred J., and Watts, Martin, *Windmills of Somerset and the men who worked them*, The Research Publishing Co., 1978.

De Little, R. J., *The Windmill yesterday and today*, John Baker (publishers) Ltd., 1972.

De Little, R. J., *The Windmills of England*, Colwood Press, 1997.

Dolman, Peter C. J., *Windmills in Suffolk: a contemporary survey*, Suffolk Mills Group, 1978.

Farries, Kenneth G., *Essex Windmills Millers & Millwrights*, Charles Skilton Ltd. (5 volumes), 1981–8.

Farries K. G., and Mason M.T., *The Windmills of Surrey and Inner London*, Charles Skilton Ltd., 1966.

Finch, William Coles, *Watermills & Windmills; A Historical Survey of their Rise, Decline and Fall as Portrayed by those of Kent*, The C. W. Daniel Company, 1933.

Flint, Brian, *Suffolk Windmills*, The Boydell Press, 1979.

Gregory, Roy, *East Yorkshire Windmills*, Charles Skilton Ltd., 1985.

Gregory, Roy, *The Industrial Windmill in Britain*, Phillimore & Co. Ltd., 2005.

Guise, Barry, and Lees, George, *Windmills of Anglesey*, Attic Books, 1992.

Hennell, Thomas, *Change in the Farm*, Cambridge University Press, 1936.

Hennell, Thomas, *The Witnesses*, Peter Davies, 1938.

Hennell, Thomas, *The Countryman at Work*, The Architectural Press, 1947.

Hills, Richard L., *Power from Wind: A history of windmill technology*, Cambridge University Press, 1993.

Hills, Richard L., *Windmills: A pictorial history of their technology*, Landmark Publishing Ltd., 2005.

MacLeod, Michael, *Thomas Hennell: Countryman, artist and writer*, Cambridge University Press, 1988.

Roberts, Jane Jo F., The Tall Tower Mills of Glamorgan, *Melin – Journal of the Welsh Mills Group*, Vol. 1, 1985, pages 3-20.

Smith, Arthur C., *Corn Windmills in Norfolk: a contemporary survey*, Stevenage Museum, 1982.

Smith, Arthur C., *Windmills in Sussex: a contemporary survey*, Stevenage Museum, 1980.

Stevens, R.D., *Cambridgeshire Windmills and Watermills*, Cambridgeshire Wind and Watermill Society, 1985.

Wailes, Rex, Essex Windmills, *Transactions of the Newcomen Society*, Volume XXXI, 1957–8 and 1958–9, pages 153–80 (+ plates).

Wailes, Rex, Lincolnshire Windmills Part II: Tower Mills, *Transactions of the Newcomen Society*, Volume XXIX, 1953–4 and 1954–5, pages 103–22 (+ plates).

Wailes, Rex, Suffolk Windmills: Part I, Post Mills, *Transactions of the Newcomen Society*, Volume XXII, 1941–2, pages 41–63 (+ plates).

Wailes, Rex, Suffolk Windmills: Part II, Tower Mills, *Transactions of the Newcomen Society*, Volume XXIII, 1942–3, pages 37–54 (+ plates).

Wailes, Rex, *The English Windmill*, Routledge & Kegan Paul Ltd., 1954.

Wailes, Rex, The Windmills of Cambridgeshire, *Transactions of the Newcomen Society*, Volume XXVII, 1949–50 and 1950–1, pages 97–119 (+ plates).

Wailes, Rex, *Tide Mills* (in two parts), Society for the Protection of Ancient Buildings, 1956.

Wailes, Rex, *Windmills in England*, Charles Skilton Ltd., 1948.

Watts, Martin, *Windmills*, Shire Publications Ltd., 2006.

West, Jenny, *The Windmills of Kent*, Skilton & Shaw, 1979 (2nd edition).

Woodward-Nutt, J., (editor), *Mills Open: windmills and watermills open to the public*, Society for the Protection of Ancient Buildings, 2004 (7th edition).